BEWILDERNESS

Reality Fiction Bred While Working in Animal Shelters

Kathleen Brown

Kearns, Howard & Walker
New York, Portland and San Francisco

Printed in the United States of America

ISBN 978-1-7354615-8-8

First Edition

14 13 12 11 10 / 10 9 8 7 6 5 4 3 2 1

Cover design by Tor Anderson

Kearns, Howard & Walker is the publishing arm of the Hubert H. & Elsie Lui Family of Students, originally established in Chicago in 1968 and subsequently based in San Francisco and the Bay Area from 1979 to the present. Administrative offices: Portland, OR/San Francisco, CA/New York, NY, United States of America. Information at www.westeastsomatics.com

Acknowledgements

Great thanks for the support and inspiration of my writing teachers: Carolyn Brigit Flynn of Writing to Feed the Soul, and Leslie Kirk Campbell of Ripe Fruit. Gratitude to writers Jean Mahoney, Lea Haratani, Dinah Davis, Celena Alison, Barbara Weigel, Kate Aver Avraham, among many others. Special thanks to N.M. Hoffmann of NYC, coach Marcy Alancraig, and editors Marilyn DuHamel and Melody Culver of Santa Cruz.

Much appreciation to my coworkers over the years, the people and the animals who wouldn't let it go, no matter how long it took.

Contents

Forward/Foreword

What does it take to walk the middle path, to move consciously on Earth, acknowledging those who are *not us* (un-human, more-than-human) in all their diversity? This may require that we seek the *us* beyond our boundaries: those who are different, the *us* that beckons our quiet, deep breathing, the *us* who move not at all or very slowly, avoiding contact. "Listen in" to the calling from somewhere close by to feel the vibration and affirmation in creating a narrative that is fundamentally inclusive, respecting all forms of life, insisting we are accountable for our actions as well as our inactions. Be willing to lift the veil, open up, and step ever so gently toward true regard, one for the other.

The telling of these stories may be exploitative, as they are based on actual people, animals, my coworkers, and events in the San Francisco, Santa Cruz and Oakland animal shelters. I worry about the moral appropriation of my storytelling. The stories are fictional composites based on actual events, with their details, characters, animals, and names changed to reflect that.

The French philosopher Vinciane Despret writes in her essay, "O for Oeuvres, Do Birds Make Art?", that if art is somehow separate from ego yet cooperative with the author's musing and intention, the work has an agency of its own. The alchemy of intersecting beings "makes me make it." As a channel for the creation of the art, I show up. This fits with my understanding of the great Taoist paradox, "where polarities meet." Now I take a deep breath and exhale within the comfort of that centered clarity.

In word and thought, my hope is to reflect the breezy gifts of beauty, wisdom and grace found in the critters themselves, interrupted now and again by a brassy bark of stormy conflict, followed by surprising connections. And I remind you, because like Ursula Le Guin, "I am much better at making things up than remembering them," the veracity of the details of these tales cannot be assured. Thus, all of this meandering is in the genre of "reality fiction."

These events could not have taken place without the host of cooperative, committed and hardworking shelter employees that I have known over the last thirty-five years. They are the most virtuous people I know. They come in three major categories: the animal control/service officers, people much too kind to be cops but with a strong sense of justice; the animal care people, consisting of attendants, behaviorists/trainers, veterinary staff, people too committed to know when to quit; and the public service representatives, the communication people who take the calls and build the language bridges to provide the service(s) requested or required. Each of them, all of them (some more than others, of course) never tire of helping whenever necessary, cleaning up urine and feces, washing laundry, opening cans and bags of food, continually showing up for the crowd of lost, injured, stray, unwanted or sick domestic and wild animals that turn up at a municipal open-door animal shelter.

Characteristically, these people are dedicated, energetic and authentically interested in serving the animals. That includes helping others of our species, homo sapiens, who walk into the shelter or wander around in public space, or find, hit, guard or own, interact or adopt, or turn in, or turn out, the beloved and bedeviled domestic animals. Our corporeal teachers, these animal beings suddenly break across sensory gates of sight, smell, touch, often through an opening of empathy, one to another.

But without the support staff (janitors, engineers, computer techs, mechanics, analysts, photographers) as well as the multifaceted volunteers, donors, critics, and public advocates (many are all of these), little of what we call *humane animal sheltering* would be possible. And while there are still many inhumane acts taking place, reform is ongoing…and incremental.

The proceeds of this book, should there be any beyond those required for publication and distribution, will be donated annually in equal parts to the three public California animal shelters described herein, in Santa Cruz, San Francisco, and Oakland, California.

⁓

This book is dedicated to canines Dulcea, Gabriel, Lulu and Mini; two cats, Fred and Ginger; and one parakeet, Maxi, all of whom accompanied me on the this journey, their gazes convincing me to write it down.

Preface/Pre-face

What do these faces look like? They are furry, feathery, whiskered, smooth, shelled and scaled—frequently domesticized mammals and birds and reptiles, but some wild and exotic wild who have arrived at central California animal shelters. Their teeth and beaks and muzzles come in all shapes and sizes. Their colors vary, but none are fluorescent and only a few are pastels; more frequently their faces are the earth tones of fungus (that which is decomposing) or autumn hues of orange, brown, black, silver-gray. Their pronouncements range from jarring, high-pitched squealing to soft squeaks, whines, whistles and moans. Some are worrisome in their silence. Many supplement vocal emanations with pacing, wiggly or frozen body language, friendly stares, tentative looks or fearful glances.

What do the eager other faces look like? The humans who tend show up in all body types, at all ages; they come in all colors, speaking varied languages, with histories and ancestry as divergent as what is held in their pockets. What is common is their concern for the welfare of animals, whether in a big city, a suburb, or on a farm, in a circus or at the city zoo.

These humans may like these animals much better than they like those of their own species. They trust the not-human animals' authenticity and unconditional acceptance. And the trust rubs off, from shared experience and actions, from kindness, attention and food. Acceptance, emotion and protective energy seal the connections each feel toward those other beings. Yet feelings of love may be a flawed projection of the human identity and psyche thrust upon those other species, those other beings, with all of the best intentions. Dilemmas of transference are everywhere in animal welfare.

Each of them, these humans that is, know that our relations *are personal.* Each of our one-on-one dealings with a specific animal is personal: an exchange of energy, a soft approach, a shared moment in the time/space continuum, sometimes a touch or a long gaze. The boundaries are permeable. However, dealing with a population of animals is a complex challenge because it may mean the life or death of the individual animal. Though personal it is, in the big picture, the wellbeing of the shelter community is paramount, and the way to protect lives. The population, the herd, the swarm, is foremost on the minds of the caregivers. Working with animals in an animal shelter is tricky, a constant triage, a negotiation, a trade-off and a risk. The tension between individual and community is an everyday deal, a bundle of responsibility with emotions as a backdrop, carried by each of us who choose to work within a shelter.

The other, *other* human faces, also of all ages, colors and backgrounds, are those whose interactions with an animal come about for one reason or another. These intersections are to be mediated in an animal shelter ecology. Together, humans give exposure and voice to competing interests—the ambiguity of shared land, space, a household, a neighborhood, a sidewalk, a park, a roadway—with a particular, *it-is-personal*, more-than-human animal, frequently, unexpectedly, right now! at these intersections. These people, members of the public, are another essential part of the equation.

And finally, we face the stampede of utilitarian order demanded by civil society in urban/suburban/rural areas. *Governmentium* taking action, often to the detriment of indigeneity, of whatever once lay native to the land, exaggerating and injecting our human exceptionalism into the landscape.

Introduction/Intro-duck-shun

Over many months I have lived a labyrinthine life during this so-called "animal stories project." I have rewritten, edited, copied and considered half a dozen formats for telling these tales. Shamed myself trying to set timelines; made oaths on my mother's grave; cursed, cried, prayed over them; sweated them out in exercise; dreamt them; became impatient, depressed, worried, and forlorn. Questioned my writing and wondered about the truth of them, the characterizations and potential exploitation of the material/the animals, my coworkers, the animal people, the institutions. Meditated, hypnotized, therapized, astrologized, divinated, self-medicated, analyzed, and begged the divine to release me from my ambivalence. Relief, I believed, could be realized only with the actualization and completion of this work.

Assuredly, it would be completed within six months of my retirement in 2013. More than seven years later, I was still working on them, insecure and unsure, my default. Daily thoughts of this storytelling, my responsibility to the material. Owing it to the animals. Owing it to my coworkers. Owing it to those who continue to experience similar interactions daily. Even owing it to you, the reader. Moreover, these stories, their animals and their people, would not relent, would not release me.

What does *project* mean? Dependent on where you put the accent. First syllable, PRO-ject—means to amplify voice. Or accent on the second syllable, pro-JECT—is an endeavor. This is both an amplification and a venture, manifest in writing. Nurture, take care, guide. In the name of doing the animals, the other, the outsider, justice.

If it is even possible to do them justice.

Further, if it is possible to animate and relate anew to the other, the animal within each of us, we have a chance for a better world.

Herein lies my prayer and best effort to date.

Initiation
Part I

Among the many species present in my childhood in the midwestern United States, I count goldfish, turtles, various insects (especially lightning bugs and mosquitoes), ground squirrels, and of course, domestic cats and dogs. But because of certain events that took place the summer of my seventh year, chipmunks hold a still point in my curious and imaginary mindscape for other beings. In a most intimate encounter, a chipmunk and my mother instructed me in the skirmish and wonder that ensues when encountering another species close up.

Ironically, my mother first taught me about protecting animals through her pronounced dislike of the three or four cats who lived up the street. Neither the cats nor their human families were well thought of by my mother. She didn't like cats who were predators, hunting, injuring and sometimes killing songbirds for sport. The fact that you allowed your cats to roam outside was reason to distrust you and your entire human family. Our neighbors, the Carters, were a particular target of Mom's ire because their cats stayed outdoors a lot. From the back porch out into the backyard, from the front door into the front yard, from her bedroom window, from the kitchen, knocking briskly on surrounding windows or shaking a broom or snapping a towel she was about to hang on the line, Mom would monitor, adamantly shooing the cats away from lounging songbirds. She was not obsessed, exactly, but very protective of those robins, cardinals and even the jays that ornamented the elm, maple and pear trees in the yard. And on one special day, the day of my grandmother's funeral, she extended that protection to include a small, scared chipmunk in a way that changed my life forever.

The animated chipmunks that kids talked about—Chip and Dale, or the singing of Alvin, Simon and Theodore—were known to me, but did not even slight ly resemble the real things, who were far more interesting and mysterious. Northern Illinois is home to the eastern *Tamais* variety of chipmunk: six to eight inches long including tail, weighing two to five ounces, with a series of stripes down a sleek, furry back and big cheeks to store food. They have light-colored underparts, dark brown eyes, a relatively bushy tail, and short front legs that are convenient for bringing food to their mouths. Their long back jumping legs have thin toes and disproportionately sized haunches that steady them when they sit back to take in the view while chowing down or scoping things out. They have long whiskers and short thick eyelashes.

My first face-to-face meeting with a live chipmunk took place during the well-attended reception at our house following the funeral for Mom's mother, our Grammy, Gertrude Decker, a member in good standing within this suburban community. Many so-called dignitaries came to pay Gram tribute: representatives from the Daughters of the American Revolution, the Episcopalian Church, the town council, friends and relatives from far and wide. But this august August day will forever be my induction into the conundrum of interspecies relationships. Little one meets a little wild one in the big theater of the front yard of our family home, with a rapt live audience in attendance.

This particular little chipmunk showed up in the mouth of a neighborhood cat, midafternoon on the day of Gram's service. The calico cat (although I didn't know the name "calico" at the time), belonging specifically to Mrs. Carter, was sassy. Sassy never ran when Mom shooed her, and she was a prolific hunter. (I think now maybe her name really was Sassy, or maybe it was our name for her. Come to think of it, Mrs. Carter was kind of sassy, too. But as a kid, of course you're not supposed to know that.)

This little chippy in the mouth of Sassy, the calico cat, spurred my seven-year-old self to action. I squatted, and calmly and sweetly called the kitty over to me. "Here, kitty, kitty..." Quiet and confident, I petted first, then restrained the cat at the nape of the neck, and miraculously, Sassy dropped her prey at my feet. The stunned chipmunk lay on her side breathing heavily with the calico still standing over the writhing furry body, watching intently. Without thinking, I gently picked up the chipmunk and cupped her in my hands for safety. The terrified animal promptly sank her teeth into the fleshy part of my left hand between index finger and thumb, latching onto me firmly and stubbornly, very strong and very alert. I remember the mixed feelings of relief and fear that washed over me. I knew something magical was going on, but this magic hurt like hell.

With the little creature locked onto my hand, I walked slowly into our house where the funeral reception was in full tilt. Groups of well-dressed adults chatted quietly, standing in somber groups or sitting with extended family in deep conversation. Holding my arm out like a summer tree limb with the eastern *Tamais* chipmunk hanging by her teeth off my hand, swinging back and forth, I tramped into the congregation. To say there was surprise in the eyes of the gathered guests would be an understatement. This was the first and only time in my life that I felt the Red Sea part in two separate human lines as I looked around desperately for help. I heard the words, "rodent," "rat," and "Bette!" (Mom's name). At the end of the parting line, there was my mom, so calm, her eyes instantly taking in the situation. She said, "Honey, we need to help this little chipmunk." There was eager agreement on my part and a collective sigh of relief from the concerned assembly.

With her firm hands holding my shoulders, Mom guided me to the solitude and quiet of the back porch. While comforting me, she cupped the body weight of the chipmunk in one hand and deftly used her thumb and index finger of the other hand to gently squeeze the jaws of the little chipmunk. The mouth opened slightly and Mom used her fingernail to release those spindly needle teeth. The frightened creature flew out of Mom's grasp, scurrying away toward the cellar as Mom leaned forward and opened her hand.

The next day I had to have a tetanus shot, like my brother did when he stepped on a rusty nail. Mom said it was about bacteria and a safety precaution. She had spent time in nursing school and knew about such things. Although we monitored the front yard for my chipmunk pal, Mom was sure the little one had moved to a different neighborhood after that close call. As the seasons changed, my animal protection instinct grew to include mice, opossum, raccoons, and of course, always the songbirds who were the gathering flocks of even more magic in the 'hood.

~~~

In the intervening threescore years, I have spotted many a chattering *Rodentia* in the form of chipmunk in Chicago, Miami, Brooklyn, Long Island, central Iowa and Milwaukee, places I settled long enough to acquaint myself with the area's native wildlife. There
~~~

were always chipmunks. However, upon relocating from the Midwest to California thirty years ago, I found that very few chipmunks lived in Santa Cruz. Squirrels, yes; but not many chipmunks. (Recently in 2019, I found that chipmunks *do* live in Ben Lomond, in the San Lorenzo Valley, within Santa Cruz County. They are a small species called Meriam's chipmunk.)

During annual hikes in the Sierra mountains, I was pleased to find chipmunks galore, chipmunks ahoy, many, many chipmunks, here and everywhere, on and off trail. I was thrilled. They were my companions over the rocks, in the woods, at the edges of the meadows, familiar like a favorite shirt, a good friend, a kind of compass of wellbeing. I began to distinguish varied species, the Lodgepole chipmunk in the low altitude valleys, and at the high altitudes the Alpine chipmunk, all the while enjoying their athleticism within the terrain. In all their chipmunk diversity, they were there in sable-striped capes, long tails sometimes curled over their bodies, captivating in their sudden appearance and stealthy disappearance, sliding into and around hidden rock holes, tree roots, dugouts. Their cheerful prudence and radical self-reliance were inspiration for the long solo treks.

After one lengthy, challenging backpacking trip in the Sierras some years ago, I decided to permanently mark myself with a special image of a chipmunk and signed up for my first animal tattoo. A two-dimensional, life-sized representation of a generic western chipmunk, a composite of the chipmunks seen in the

Sierra Nevada, now graces my right shoulder, commemorating a lifelong journey of learned humility when animals come before my eyes.

(Initiation - Part II at the close of this book)

Making Do With Doo-Doo

What do you do when you have found an injured bird on the beach, a stray dog wandering in the park, or a skinny, greasy-coated cat on your doorstep? Maybe you have hit a squirrel with your car, or you come upon injured wildlife at a gas station while on the road. Whether a kitten in the automobile engine, a mouse in the electric wiring, or a snake wrapped around the cylinder, animal crossings transport us into another dimension, outside predictability, and often provide an on-ramp to altered consciousness on the one-way street to our emotions.

What do you do when you spot a trapped bird in the window well or flying around Safeway, hear an opossum behind the bathroom wall, or surprise a litter of newborn kittens in the garage? Maybe you are the one the neighbors call or the kids seek, the one who seems to know what to do with the approach of a frightened or frightening woolly spider, egg-bound hen, stunned raptor or lost dog. These things happen. Or perhaps you are the neighbor who seems cued into animals, attuned to what is happening to other living creatures in your environment. When you can't find that neighbor or you need animal help, you call animal services in your community.

If so, statistics indicate the probability that you are a woman, more relational it is believed, and you probably have donated to an animal welfare cause during the course of your life. Again, as a woman, statistics show that an animal rights or animal protection agency will solicit your attention and your support, your money is an important asset. Adopters and donors to animal shelters, as well as volunteers, are four times as likely to be women. There are approximately 5,000 animal shelters in the United States, averaging 100 shelters per state; of course some are better than others, and many of them are staffed predominantly by women workers. Many North American and European animal shelters model their programs after those in central California. San Francisco is one of the best places in the world to be a domestic animal in a shelter. The Bay Area has a reputation of leadership in the field.

~

In 2010, women occupied 78% of the seats in veterinary schools throughout the United States; at University of California at Davis it was 83%. Interestingly, veterinary medicine is becoming a soft science as more women gain admission to veterinary medical schools. There are more women veterinarians than males in the United States. The median income in 2009 for a female vet was $79,000 while it was $109, 000 for a male vet, suggesting that as females gain access to the field, incomes decrease and the work becomes less lucrative. There is a Shelter Medicine track in the Doctor of Veterinary Medicine (DVM) program for students interested in working in the shelter environment. Nonprofit organizations are staffed by 75 percent women, according to a 2015 *Forbes Magazine* study. From my experience, the professions of animal technicians/nurses, behaviorists, zookeepers, breeders, groomers, dog walkers and animal trainers also attract women in disproportionate numbers because they are more likely to embrace the ethics of caregiving over their male counterparts. This is consistent with job statistics published by the United States Department of Labor in 2015.

In sixteenth-century Europe, domestic livestock were taken up and taken in by village authorities consistent with early property laws. Animals were income. Holding places for animals were named "pounds" (perhaps for the animal's monetary value), where lost and wandering livestock were kept with the intention of returning them to a rightful owner, usually an aristocrat farmer or herder. Cows, goats, sheep, horses were the charges of the "poundmaster."

With Western industrialization and urbanization in the 1820s, the first humane (animal welfare) societies looked to aid abused and overwrought horses, unable to ignore that some animals needed protection from their "owners." Forty years later, in the midst of the buildup to the Civil War, not only was there the political movement toward abolition of slavery, but we also saw the first animal shelters open their doors in New York City, Philadelphia and San Francisco. (Notably, humane societies began advocating for child-labor laws and for youngsters to have the same rights as neglected and abused beasts of burden like ox, mules and horses.) Domesticated dogs were included in the mix and began to be protected at the turn of the century; in the nineteen twenties and thirties, cats were also taken in. Today, animal shelters are sometimes referred to as "pounds," a legal term still used in ordinances and law books. The word is casually used by the media and the public as a slur, a devaluation by implication, of the animal protection work done at your local animal shelter.

~

The quality of public tax-supported animal shelters is dependent upon where you live, the activists in town, the economy, and the politics of the time. Historically, animal-related laws reflect public health and public safety concerns, particularly dog bites and rabies exposure with dog and other mammal bites to humans, resulting in mandated reports to authorities. By the end of the twentieth century, however, shelter mission statements changed focus from property rights and human safety to the consideration of the moral standing of Animalia in postmodern culture, with the emphasis moving from shelter as jail to shelter as adoption center for common domesticated household animals. The "depository" for animals (the actual term used in California state law for animal shelters) became a holding center as well as a hospital. The animal shelter evolved into an agency providing intervention and respite for animals in lost, stray, injured, neglected scenarios. You traveled from hell to limbo to purgatory to redemption, if you were "a lucky dog."

Shelters are a mix of prison and hospital, administered under efficiency concepts, health considerations and systems of "herd management," in veterinary terms. That's utilitarian-speak for "The greatest good for the greatest number." Consideration must be given to those continuing to enter the herd in an open-door shelter. Appropriate sanitary space will be needed for the newly admitted and resources will be used to administer to illness or injury and to achieve and maintain good health; to do no harm. To try to get them back home.

Many types of animals are served in today's animal shelters. From livestock to exotic reptiles and birds, to wildlife, to "pocket pets" such as guinea pigs, hamsters and chinchillas, to the ubiquitous dogs and cats, all are dependent upon the values, articulate advocates, and wherewithal (funding) of a given community. With new animal protection laws, many animal shelters in the United States have developed their programs under public funding, which is usually sparse. Those programs last as long as the funding lasts, until the next austerity campaign. Enhancements and enrichments come by virtue of the cadre of volunteers who insist on improving quality of life for the animals lodged in animal shelters.

Overall, animals in shelters live in a kind of crazy town for them: confined overstimulation, smelly, loud and chaotic, with those in need coming and going 24/7. This can be hell for animals whose senses are complex and may be quickly overwhelmed. The critters may shut down, freak out, vocalize, pace, and some die. Not many thrive.

In order to advocate for a better shelter environment, we routinely don our political boots, badges and uniforms to go to council meetings to advocate for increased funding. We write letters, sign petitions, protest outdated equipment, and celebrate results when more stringent laws are passed, locally or statewide, to protect our animal friends both domestic and wild. But without the financial wherewithal—that is, procuring a budget sufficient to maintain and improve standards of care, to increase staff, and to offer more training, education and enforcement to address changing needs, resources and vision—our best efforts are reactionary and ineffective. Burnout ensues.

Deeply disturbed by the influx of population and the inconsistency of providing a high standard of care, we "make do." Burnout expands.

Frequently, well-intentioned fly-by-the-seat-of–her-pants nonprofit "rescue" operations rise up to fill the void. They do amazing work to help all kinds of animals, all kinds of ways.

These groups work to move those animals from the shelter into foster homes. They save many lives, from snakes to ducks, mostly dogs and cats at risk of falling through the cracks, particularly those unable to adjust to the shelter environment. These volunteer rescue groups operate in passionate and sometimes naïve attempts to save domestic pets from perceived, and sometimes real, abuse and destruction of animals at their local shelter. In this work, a growing self-imposed bundle of expectation results in burgeoning responsibility and an endless supply of what is perceived as adversarial conflict with shelters, which may result in mistrust, blame and disinformation.

Humans carry deep ambivalence toward animals. One major thing: we eat them. We also hunt them, ride them, stuff them, wear their fur, walk on their skin, live with them, train them and display them; we dominate them for our benefit, we humanize them, we demonize them. And some of us say, loudly and often, that we love them.

As a result of all of this, the shelter—temporary refuge or home for the unwanted, lost, sick or injured (mostly dogs and cats, but oh, so much more)—balances on a wobbly cultural tightrope. The shelter represents a panoply of institutions for animals, from pet shop to zoo, from jail to sanctuary, from orphanage to hospice. And it carries on a range of functions, from animal behavior to social work, from education to record keeping, from housing to euthanasia. Our communities have put forth impossible expectations. For those of you who care, you have expressed that you expect animal caregivers to stand in your stead. And stand we do.

For others of you, less understandably, you dislike the frisky dogs, squawking parrots and burrowing rodents. And shelter workers will stand for your right to be safe from the fear of animals you don't know or care to know. We may ask you to support us in learning to coexist with them while we try to explain why they do what they do. And while we affirm that respect for their agency, their right to a full life, albeit a shared life, is at the very least part of the answer.

The San Francisco animal care facility moved into a renovated Art Deco 1920s building in the center of the industrial Mission District in 1988, when the San Francisco Society for the Prevention of Cruelty to Animals (SFSPCA), one of the oldest and well-known humane societies in the United States, determined they no longer wanted to contract for animal control functions. The City hired folks away from the SPCA to make a shelter San Francisco could be proud of. It took a year to convert a materials warehouse of 15,000 square feet into an animal shelter. This two-story concrete building is held together with huge, six-foot-circumference, weight-bearing columns like pilings that run the height of the building, carrying its stress. Dated twelve-foot-high chicken-wire reinforced glass windows provide the kennels with natural light and fresh air on either side of the building. Filled to the brim with cages, small and large metal containment fences, baby gates, crates, towels, blankets and pillows, this shelter houses up to 300-350 animals on a daily basis, carrying all that emotional and physical stress. This is a building bursting with both love and fear. Accommodations, Spartan; bedding, clean; and the food is good. Much of the rest is unknown.

The lighting is fluorescent and the brightly colored thick enamel paint is scored, scratched and scarred by a history of animal paw hieroglyphics. Thorough cleaning is done daily with power washers and disinfectant in dog kennels. All other cleaning is done by hand. The on-site laundry facilities operate nonstop. The huge air exchange systems on the roof condition and rotate the air in the shelter every ten minutes; at least that is the promise. Nightmares come in the form of contagious disease outbreak, fire, flood and dog mauling, in that order. What the animals dream is unknown to this writer; still, when asleep, they twitch and whine and paw the air. Dealing with day-to-day reality seems quite enough for most of them.

Down the long hallways of the kennels, strained and quiet human voices speak a library of shelter terms: rescue, save, temperament, behavior, breed, spay, neuter, vaccinate, and spoken softly in a kind of whispered prayer—looking around, not to be overheard—euthanasia. In the lobby, voices speak in louder, outsized vocabulary where you can and want to be overheard: adoption, redemption, fees, surgery, pick up, money, citation, time, when, what and how. In the law enforcement division tucked away upstairs, you hear crackling voices over the radio and on the mobile phone speaking officious jargon: respond, citation, case, detail, emergency, vehicle, van, report, officer, abuse, evidence, DA, safety, follow-up. In the veterinary clinic: X-rays, meds, discharge, records, parasites, pathogens, tests, pain, antibiotics, surgery, supplies. In administration the words are formed very slowly and carefully in proper grammar: public, letter, complaint, mediate, donor, budget, program, funding, volunteer, education, downtown, city hall.

In the background dogs bark, moan, howl intermittently. Parrots squawk, birds cheep, cats meow and hiss, guinea pigs whistle, hamsters turn in the drone of their wheels. The air handlers and pumps whirl on the roof, the metal garage doors roll open, the hoses swoosh in the kennels and the washing machines spin, vibrating and spiraling through the final cycle.

Generally, the animal caregivers, the animal technicians, the veterinarians, the assistants, the animal cops, the coordinators, administrators and managers, the people who work in shelters describe themselves as animal lovers and animal people. Often that means that they resonate more with animals than with others of their own species. They care deeply about the plight of animals in an urban/suburban white middle-class kind of way.

Middle-class values seem to dominate in animal shelters across Northern California. On one side, the property owners want order, safety, peace and quiet; the white privileged want to bring their dogs into Whole Foods or on BART. On one hand, domestic animals are a nuisance; on the other, they are part of the family. There is a continuous tension between the two.

In shelters where workers reflect a wider ethnicity and working-class values, ongoing struggle with and discussion of the value of animals exists along and far beyond the middle-class ethical spectrum. It only just begins with carnivore, vegetarian or vegan questions. In San Francisco, shelter workers are not only Anglo Northern European white but also Mexican, Central, South, and African American, Chinese, Korean, Native American, Samoan, and Filipino. Black, brown, white, humans in every color, like their counterparts the animals, are from all walks of life along every socioeconomic strata. As policies and laws reflect the mayors, supervisors, lawmakers and those in power, capitalist middle-class values prevail in many of these shelters, with ethics reflecting animals as close relatives at one end, or as property, a nuisance or a threat at the other. Humane societies and nonprofit shelters lean toward understanding animals as family members and are often more progressive on the more-than-human spectrum.

The animal shelter staff responds to all kinds of requests, demands, determinations, definitions and difficulties brought both courtesy of city hall policies and politics as well as by animal guardians, animal advocates, animal activists, animal-interested parties, and animal owners. These hominids can be described with as many emotional adjectives as there are books in the Library of Congress and endless combinations of these variables: indifferent, thoughtless, compassionate, drugged out, bureaucratic, distraught, happy, mean, grateful, entitled, bossy, caring, difficult, lying, crying, whining, defeated. From gangster to opera star, from elderly Vietnam veteran to Nob Hill real estate lady, from academic to meth addict, people's lives intersect with animals' lives in many United States cities, small towns and unincorporated areas.

Fittingly, nonhuman animal species, including fish, birds and insects, outnumber us. Recent microbial research indicates that the Kingdom of Animalia comprises only about 1% of life by weight on planet Earth. Our likenesses are completely overshadowed 1,000 times, not only by species of plant life but also by complex single-cell bacteria that live everywhere on the planet in the water, the soil, and the atmosphere. Lichen, a combination of bacteria, fungi and algae, covers approximately 6% of the earth's surface, while we cover only 1%. Lichen is believed to be immortal; luckily for all, we are not.

However, mammalian predators are the biological faction closest to us, and on Earth in the twenty-first century, we have them outnumbered by 4,000 to one. And yet these wise relatives have so much to teach us. They hold the precarious position of illustrating complex biological, chemical, socio-economic, ethnic, ecological, and historical realities. As well, they demonstrate the interdependence of all of those realities. They point to the evolution and devolution of our relationship to and understanding of diverse forms of life, visible and invisible. They expand what it means to think, to be intelligent, to share resources with those who lived long before we got here and will likely survive in some form long after our passing. I find great comfort in that likelihood.

My career in animal welfare began in 1985, selling dog licenses at the Santa Cruz SPCA. Soon promoted to an animal care attendant, I spent my days cleaning the kennels, learning animal husbandry, attending classes about animal health, and assisting the medical staff with sick or injured dogs and cats. After overseeing the physical needs of the animals in the shelter for a couple of years, I became an animal control and humane officer. One of the stories in this book is about my challenges as an officer in Santa Cruz during the Loma Prieta earthquake in 1989. Eventually, I rose to managerial positions and after thirteen years, left Santa Cruz for San Francisco, where I was hired as the Deputy Director of San Francisco Animal Care & Control (SFACC).

Admittedly, the stories of being an administrator in the SF animal shelter are at least as much about people as they are about the animals. The order of story placement in the book is intentional, to reflect the way that uncertainty guides, or rather *dictates*, the activities within an animal shelter. You never know who is going to walk in the door, who will be on the phone, what the next dispatched call may bring. These encounters are also about the vulnerability of being present with and for the animals at those intersections where there are limited or no traffic signals. In what follows, you will experience just some of the many and varied stories of lives in the crosswalk. Each has a basis in fact with the names changed to provide anonymity for individuals, or to protect the people and agencies with whom I was employed. I have taken occasional creative liberty with the facts to present a composite of my experience, with the caveat that those experiences garnered from the past will undoubtedly contain some fiction.

These accounts are offered as a tribute to apex predators like us as well as to the undervalued among us, the other, human and the more-than-human.

I attempt to bring some clarity to what is often overlooked or hidden. I hope you may learn something from them as I have, as knowledge is power. Knowledge also brings responsibility.

Pot Pit

Very early one warm summer morning in August, a Santa Cruz County communications dispatcher contacted me by phone at home to say that I was needed on a call to support the county sheriff's office. She told me to get in my vehicle and drive up Highway 9, and that she would let me know the exact location of the action. She apologized that it was 4:30 am and that she couldn't tell me the details of the call. The overnight on-call officer for emergencies for the Santa Cruz shelter covered the hours from 11:30 pm until 7 am. And that was me.

Rookie animal control officer, I was hardly wet behind the ears and yawned into the phone. Donning a khaki-colored uniform shirt with identifying shoulder patches, jeans and construction boots, it didn't take long to get dressed. My uniform also included a thick black leather belt around my waist with a two-way radio and a long metal flashlight hooked on a brass ring attached to the belt. That flashlight took nine D-cell batteries, hung heavy from my waist to my knees, and doubled as a bite stick. On call, we were to wear a heavy brown nylon jacket with a badge, but it was late summer and that jacket was just plain out of season.

I shook myself awake, threw the jacket onto the passenger seat, climbed into my blue puppy-paw identified white Ford van, and headed up to the San Lorenzo Valley along twisted, two-lane redwood-laden Highway 9.

Somewhere near Ben Lomond, about 10-12 miles up Highway 9 from Santa Cruz, I contacted the dispatcher by radio, announced my location and asked for further direction. County communications nonchalantly told me to continue up Highway 9 and I would receive further instructions at Big Basin Way, also known as Highway 236. Usually when we were dispatched on a call, we were told what and where it was, but not today. It was all a mystery.

Dawn light was breaking over the mountains and it was a beautiful morning for a drive. When I got to Boulder Creek, a tiny mountain town, county communications contacted me to tell me to take a left up Big Basin Way to the state park at Big Basin. At this point, I realized they were tracking my location. At the park, dispatch communications told me to continue up 236 and announced that there was now radio silence. A few miles past the park, I began to see soldiers in camouflage uniforms with tree branches protruding from the top of their combat helmets. These soldiers were in the brush on the side of the road carrying AK47s, or whatever the assault weapon du jour was in 1987. I began to get nervous. A few of the soldiers walking on the road waved me along. I drove for at least another twenty minutes on Highway 236, then a checkpoint appeared at a gravel road to my right. The fully armed and uniformed troops told me to drive up the road where I would be met by the team leader, who would give me my assignment.

What was I getting into?

The sun was just coming up. As instructed, I drove to the end of the gravel road, where various military and police vehicles were parked and a few guys were standing around with federal DEA (Drug Enforcement Administration) agents and ATF (Alcohol, Tobacco and Firearms) officers, duly noted with monikers emblazoned on the back of their light summertime black jackets. I parked my van, puffed myself up, threw on my heavy brown nylon jacket like a cape and strutted over to the military guys. Gotta have your jacket. Police and the sheriff were there as well as detectives in plainclothes with badges and guns. A helicopter flew low overhead. With no introductions, I gave the guy who addressed me my business card. He motioned for me to follow him, saying that it was a drug bust. We hiked ten minutes up a trail to a clearing and approached a single-story ranch house with no windows in front at all and a huge double-sized redwood door. A young bearded man was sitting outside with a full-backed toilet as a seat, about ten yards from the door. His arms were pulled behind the tank and he was handcuffed. There must have been twenty agents milling about with clipboards, black boxes that looked like fishing tackle kits, big black plastic bags and notebooks.

The team leader told me that I was to remove rattlesnakes from the pit near the front door so they could enter and search the residence. My jaw dropped, I'm sure. He pointed toward the door. A three-foot-deep snake pit was dug underneath the threshold to the front door. Inside this three-foot-wide concrete pit were dozens of young rattlesnakes. The restrained, bearded man spoke up suddenly, "They want to shoot the snakes. I knew you would come and get them." Hesitantly, I told him I would do my best.

The military, the cops and the DEA/ATF were afraid of the rattlesnakes. The young man told them that he would catch them and set them free, but they refused to allow that. The powers-that-be wanted those snakes gone. And their removal was my assignment.

Now I had to figure out how to get them out of there. Snake tongs were standard in the van, but I don't really remember how I captured those snakes. I know I had a shovel and a couple of 5-gallon buckets, and I found a third bucket at the house. I had a couple of nets for catching birds and small mammals, and some bungee cords. The guys stood back and didn't help, making like they were busy, talking in small groups.

I got the snakes into the buckets. One at a time, I hauled a bucket with ten or twelve snakes in it, covered by my jacket, back down the trail to the parked van, covered each bucket with a net, and put a bungee cord around the top.

I made three trips. Finally the pit was empty. The entourage was breaking down the door to enter the building. The team leader thanked me. "Nice job," he said as he turned away.

Slowly walking back to my van, I thought I was going to pee myself. The cops and guards were all around but I didn't care, I pulled down my pants and peed the longest, most satisfying pee ever. I got in the van and backed down the gravel road. While doing so, I realized there was another dilemma: Would the rattlesnakes, *could* the rattlesnakes get out of those precarious snake-habitat five-gallon buckets I'd fabricated? Rattlesnakes can squeeze themselves through very small openings. That worry accompanied me back down winding Highway 236 and Big Basin Way, down Highway 9, through the San Lorenzo Valley, and back to the Santa Cruz shelter in Live Oak. The drive must have taken more than an hour and a half while I kept an eye on those buckets in my rearview mirror, listening for any rattling. I watched the floor of the van as much as I did the road, all the way back down the mountain.

When I pulled into the rear parking lot of the shelter, I was extremely relieved. It seemed I'd made the trip successfully without mishap. After checking the status of my snake payload, my boss met me at the back gate. It was after 9 am and the workday had just begun for everyone else on staff. No one knew of my adventure, as radio silence was maintained before 9 am. My boss asked where I'd been. Telling her the beginning of the story as I began unloading the animals from the van, I showed her the rattlesnakes in one of the buckets. She swore loudly, "Fuck! Get those snakes out of here." Totally flipped out, she told me angrily that they were a huge liability. What was I thinking? They needed to be relocated back in the San Lorenzo Valley.

I was mortified; I hadn't thought beyond my destination, not at all. It had not even occurred to me; but, of course, that would be the correct course of action. I loaded the snake buckets back into the van and went back up Highway 9 to secluded and little-traveled Felton Empire Grade Road, worrying the entire forty-five minutes if the snakes would stay in their white buckets. The rattlesnakes cooperated with me that day as I found a remote turnout way up Empire Grade, removed the bungees, pulled off the netting and tipped each bucket, three separate times, thanking my lucky stars. Returning to the shelter, not to challenge destiny any further, I unloaded everything in the van to make sure an outlier rattlesnake had not surreptitiously escaped her makeshift bucket for liberation under the driver's seat.

What does it mean to be a dog catcher? The image of an overweight guy with a net chasing after Lady and the Tramp? Those days are over.

Much more to come.

Bump
My Friends and My Fears

Some mornings, imagined bats fly out of the sink toward me. I see the shadowy creatures in the corner of my eye and duck slightly out of their way as they ascend the pitch toward hiding places in the rafters. Other days, I am awakened by the croak of a frog, the howl of a coyote or the hoot of an owl.

Listening hard, I wait for the message. Is that a guinea pig whistle I hear? Other mornings, in the company of a symphony of domestic animals—goats, cats, chickens, and maybe something like spilled hibiscus tea from the night before, now congealed on the counter like blood from the veins of the cold room—I am crimson. Some mornings the muse sleeps in and dreams. Later, this awakening dog guardian finds not just fur and dust, floaters and motes, but the banality of flea dirt, dried tiny spots.

In my consciousness, in my conscience, lives the Other. I like to think it is an "I/Thou" discourse somehow informed by curiosity and a life of spirit seeking.

On bad days, I know the source of this struggle is the guilt of my very personal original sin and the deaths of hundreds of animals who have died at my hand, whether eaten or euthanized, the deaths of the animals that died in my arms while being treated, found injured, neglected or euthanized. Defensively, I know what that means but I wrestle with mixed metaphors, anthropomorphism, giving voice and moral status to the multitude of creatures that flap, fly, forage and stalk. Especially in the morning, those fleeting souls reach me in the early hours when their voices and ghostly wailing are most haunting. I am burning with the blood orange need to tell the story.

This week is made up of Charley and Red and Mara and Tiny. But today Bump is on my mind.

I can't tell you why Bump died. It was not for lack of our trying. What I can say is this: Bump lived a short life as a hermit crab in a paper cup on the dashboard of a vintage Chevy Nova, cared for by Melissa, an aging and frail homeless woman with kidney disease. The hermit crab, just a slight bit larger than a California brown garden snail, was named Bump. As guardian to Bump, Melissa lived for her crustacean companion; she truly adored that crab.

"Born under Cancer, we are alike," she'd say. On a chilly winter night in San Francisco, Melissa collapsed and fell seriously ill. She'd clashed with the EMTs after her call to 911, insisting that the animal shelter staff meet her at her car, that she would not leave Bump in the car unattended in the Tenderloin neighborhood off Market Street. Within an hour, she was in renal failure and at General Hospital in a coma. Homeless advocates notified us of Bump's whereabouts. Bump the hermit crab was in a paper cup on the dashboard of Melissa's old Chevy Nova. Bump came into protective custody at our animal shelter that night.

Three days later, when Melissa awoke and left the hospital without a doctor's release, she immediately came to our shelter. She still had the needle from the IV in the vein above her wrist. We had to tell her that Bump was dead. We had saved his crusty little carcass and we handed Bump's remains to Melissa over the counter in the lobby, wrapped in a donated washcloth. "God rest his little soul," we said to her. Melissa wailed deeply and left this public space in great despair, holding her Bump, her swaddled crab, to her chest.

Within a couple of hours, Melissa called me on the phone to say that she was *very* upset. After leaving the shelter and in the privacy of the automobile that was their home, Melissa unwrapped Bump's body. She noticed the telltale dark-brown, almost black exudate coming from "his hole." She said Bump had died an awful death, she just knew it; she could tell he'd been stressed. Melissa told me that he "turned dark in his hole" only when he was anxious.

I told her how sorry I was for her loss...that I was very concerned about the role that we may have played in Bump's suffering and demise. I would look into what had happened in the course of our care for him at our animal shelter. I would call her right back.

And so I did. This is what I found.

When Bump came to us in his paper cup, we diligently researched the care and diet of a hermit crab on the Internet. The optimum diet for a hermit crab is carnivorous. We went up the block to Safeway to purchase the "right" diet and fed him morsels of steak, ground round and free-range chicken. He was housed in an expansive reptile tank with a pond, sand and rocks as recommended by science, ocean entomologists and animal experts. He had amphibian/reptile hiding places in tropical heat and a Pacific environment. Telling her of our efforts to care for Bump, Melissa's convulsive cries on the phone only increased. "Bump was used to a paper cup, he ate only hotdogs, listened to country music and sat in the sun on the dashboard of my Chevy. Every once in a while, I would turn on the heat in the car." She repeated that she only fed Bump wieners from the corner store and worms when she could find them on the sidewalk near the park after it rains.

Obviously, our attempts to care for Bump had gone awry. We thought to feed Bump the "right food" and create the "right habitat" and failed miserably by Bump and Melissa's standards. Frustrated and distraught, I offered to replace Bump to fill the silence on the phone line. I knew the offense of my brittle proposal before the final syllables crossed my lips. Melissa regained her composure and brusquely told me we would hear from her attorney. Then came the abrupt click of disconnect.

To this day, her grief, her care for beloved Bump, and the lesson learned remain alive in me...sometimes turning me dark in my hole. We know so little about the lives of others, what nurtures them and under what circumstances they thrive.

~~~

This chronicles the beginning of a close encounter with mystery. *Mystery.* A word that means "that which is outside understanding." I wish I knew. I wish I could tell you what is behind this "bumpy" ride. Maybe in the end, life and love is all about relationships. We thrive in relation to one another no matter our environment or diet, reflecting our unique entanglement with one another, bumping up against one another, creating a unity of connection, framed by love and sometimes by awe.

And so I must write up these stories, based in fact, told true sometimes. I try them on, see if they work, for me, for them, for us; does it make sense? I want to know, *hmmm*, let me see, it is *this*? Is it *that* becomes *this?* All the queries remind me of habits of trying to guess the feelings, thoughts and motivations of the animate, the animals, trees, plants, the thoughts and motivations of my mentally ill brother, my confused parents, my schoolmates, friends and sexual partners, in our exploratory journeys of interdependencies.

The investigation can only continue. "We will work on this puzzle," I tell staff. "We work to expose this
~~~

mystery, not to solve it." Childlike, the reports and conversations line up in pieces of disorder on my desk. But these events are real; the ideas, these mysteries are bigger than me. They own me. They work through me, they are channeled through me in some great synchronicity with beingness. The others, more-than-human (whatever that means) insisting, turning us around and holding onto us while we walk the backstreets of the famed urban monolith of San Francisco. These thoughts, these stories are found objects amid the observed detritus of an overturned shopping cart behind the office supply store: worn Nikes, old wool blankets, sweaters, torn jeans, discarded t-shirts, soiled underwear. Unafraid today that beneath it all, there is a jewel: the testament may be a dark song, a rhythmic hint that accompanies enchantment leading to a hint, a clue, that comes with paying attention, listening to the humble, daring to witness the other.

Is it any wonder that the difference between "mystery" and "my-story" is just one letter of the alphabet, an "o"? That's an *Ohhhh...just the very beginning of Other.*

CocoaBellaChocolates Shopping Bag Message

I've been walking around in a daze for days, lifeless, lively-less, joyless and sad. I had an appointment on Wednesday, March 20, to have Daisy's tumor removed. She was having a bad day last week and I brought her into your shelter on Tuesday, March 12 at approximately 11:00 am. Judy was working and said Daisy'd be fine.

They're my lifeline. They make me tick. They bring me peace. I share them with people every day and everyone loves them, young and old alike.

These last four days have been hell on me but I kept the faith that you would see the truth. I take them on Pier 39 every night to visit the sea lions. In the day I go to the park and they roll in the grass. I'm a simple man (KISS). I'm not that smart but I know how to treat people with respect. "Do unto others…" You know, "assume = ASS-YOU-ME."

Rumors can kill and lies change lives. I'm fifty-one years old (2/22/62, lucky 2s) on my birthday a couple weeks ago. I was telling everybody I was a 5150 nut case, and maybe I am. But I would never harm them in any way. I'm out of tears but will go on. I tried to be a good guy and pray I remain the same. I love to make people happy. I don't like me without my kids. I'm at the mercy of you. I'm begging for mercy. Please. The source of the complaint, Steve, told me he was in prison. The one telling everybody I kicked Pickles. He's a liar.

I'm a man of peace, love, joy. San Francisco is my favorite city in the United States. It gives me peace of mind. It's safe and clean. My heart is here. I'd do anything in the world to help someone. I'm a pussycat in a dog's body. My conscience is clear. My life destroyed. My heart has been shattered. Lies have destroyed so many lives. I've been labeled an animal abuser, which is far from the truth. I am a people person, a dog person. I smell like hell, look like hell and have bad breath, but I'd never do anything to harm my babies. You could offer me a million dollars or the dogs back, I'd take the dogs.

My first Dalmatian, Daisy, was from San Diego, California in 1994. Nineteen years, I have no history of ever mistreating animals. Look how good they look. I'd never hit or kicked a dog in my life. I didn't know how good I had it until I lost them, my best friends in the whole world. I'm soul searching. I will take a polygraph test.

I hate to say it but I love the dogs more than people. I've been a nervous wreck. Ask anybody at the wharf. I got here in 1997. Seventeen years. I don't do drugs, just drink. I love this city. I abuse myself, not the dogs. They offer the world to me. No family or friends. I haven't eaten or slept right for four days. I know who called animal control to complain. Steve, with the dog named Brother. My accuser, where is he?

I will do anything to get them back. Work, pay or AA. They call me the Dogman. At the wharf, I dress like a dog, a Dalmatian like Daisy, and panhandle while holding Pickles in a tutu. When I set her down, she will dance on her back legs. People enjoy this, enjoy them. Daisy and Pickles have fun. If I was doing anything wrong, we would not have lasted seventeen years. I've been riding the F train just to kill time. I live in a van at the wharf. I walk them every day, rain or shine. I feed them before I eat. I feel like my heart has been ripped out.

I thought I was a people person but I'm not. I'm an animal person. I love dogs. My dogs are like people. I love people dogs better than dog people. I am Dogman.

Bugged and Beleaguered

She showed up in the middle of the night wearing a formal gown and cowboy boots. The woman carried her two-year-old gray calico cat, Liz, in a hard-shell cat carrier that was too small. The carrier was not too small for *a* cat, but Liz at twenty-two pounds was too big for that normal-sized cat carrier. Holding the tipping carrier at the door of the all-night emergency veterinary hospital on Fillmore Street, Marcy was talking to herself, or maybe to her cat. Middle-aged, red-headed, swarthy, loud and intense, Marcy was "a sight to behold," recorded the veterinary technician.

She brought her cat to the veterinarian because of the bugs. Marcy said Liz the cat had fleas, worms and other parasites that left her house in St. Francis Woods bug-infested, and worse than that, she feared, the bugs had moved from Liz to Marcy. The prescribed pyrethrin topical medication was not working, had not worked for days. In desperation, Marcy had applied diatomaceous earth and lime to Liz's underside. The bugs were still there.

After the night vet on duty examined Liz, he told Marcy to go home, that they would keep Liz overnight for monitoring. In the morning, the vet called the animal shelter to report possible animal abuse. They sent over the examination report that described Marcy's demeanor, Liz's severe hair loss, and the chemical burns and serious skin inflammation on the cat's belly. Liz was having a strong reaction to unknown substances apparently spread onto her body by her owner/ guardian in order to address what was described by her owner as a major bug infestation. On the battery of tests designed to find parasites and fleas, Liz tested negative.

In the interview at her home, Marcy acknowledged that she was doing everything she could think of to alleviate the bugs that proliferated in the home environment. She appeared cheerful and upbeat. Her very sparsely decorated living room consisted of wooden dining room chairs, three lamps, a long walnut coffee table with a TV on it, and a new leather upholstered recliner chair, still in the opened box. The wall-to-wall carpeting had been unceremoniously torn up and lay rolled up outdoors in her driveway. Carpet tacks held remnants of spongy padding and loose wool threads outlined the perimeter of the room, thick in the corners of the dull, scratched oak flooring, into the vestibule and leading up the stairs. The black, scorched area over the fireplace suggested a misguided effort to smoke out the bugs in the house. Marcy provided the receipt from the exterminator who had debugged the residence a couple of weeks before our interactions and subsequent interview. He had returned to her house multiple times, she told us. Then Marcy showed us the kitchen that smelled strongly of Lysol, where she no longer kept food because she had found bugs in the flour and yogurt.

When asked about the bugs on her cat, she became quiet. Marcy said that she'd lied to the vet about the cat being infested because that was the only way she could get her cat treated. The bugs, she believed, were from the house. She thought the original infestation began with her stay at an elite hotel on Nob Hill approximately six months prior, when the bugs attached to her fur coat. Marcy discovered the insects just a week or so before her husband left her. "I can't believe he left me in this pickle," she said. "I've collected some of the bugs and sent them to the entomologists at the University of Wisconsin in Madison. I should have the results any day now. I've done everything the exterminator recommended. But they are still here. Maybe you can help me?"

During the next few days, we became involved in identifying through the Internet the bugs that Marcy brought to us in envelopes, pillboxes and matchboxes. While waiting for the report from the lab in Wisconsin, she had surreptitiously gone back to the hotel and gained entrance to one of the rooms on the same floor as the room she had stayed in. The bugs she brought us in their little containers looked like bedbugs to us. She said they were from the posh hotel on Nob Hill. This information would be scandalous, if true.

In the following days and weeks, Marcy provided us with much "evidence" of her fight against the bugs. She had a file of receipts from pest control to painters and housecleaners, to the furriers where her coats were now safely stored after being debugged. She removed all upholstered furniture and sent all clothing out to be cleaned; all her bedding was washed two or three times *a day*. She hired waste management to deliver a dumpster, removing furniture and carpeting. She said she had worked for years as a career coach for a well-known headhunter firm down on Market Street until she and her husband struck out on their own. She gave us her business card. She told us the business had been failing over the course of the last year, the final nail in the coffin when her husband began an affair with a younger woman in the office and left Marcy after twelve years of marriage. Now fifty and losing some of her allure, Marcy couldn't compete with the younger woman, she opined. We waited for the lab report and statement from the vet, checked on her business license, tried to corroborate her story and tie up loose ends in the case.

Her bizarre wardrobe the night of the veterinary visit resulted from her attempt to contain the bugs. The gown and boots were the only garments she owned that were not bug-infested, as they came directly from her car and the dry cleaners. That night, she had been so worried about Liz and couldn't wait until morning.

She loved Liz and wanted her back. She was lonely without Liz. It all sounded very plausible. No one else believed her.

Returning Liz to Marcy seemed risky. How would she keep Liz safe from the bugs? Did Marcy truly understand that the homegrown treatment for her cat could be harmful and dangerous? We told her we couldn't return her cat to her at this time, as we needed to proceed with further investigation. We asked if she had any other character witness or family that could help her with Liz, maybe her ex-husband, that we could talk to. With some hesitation, she gave us her ex's name and phone number. She had a sister in Marin. "Would it be better if we talked to her?" we asked. She looked down at her feet, now in pumps, to match her rumpled business suit. "Well, maybe..." she said, "...but they don't believe me." She appeared distracted. Again, she said, "They don't believe me." She began to say something else, then began crying softly. The meeting ended abruptly and she left the building. Within an hour, Marcy lawyered up. We heard from her attorney that all further communication in the case was to take place through him.

Bedbugs are mentioned in ancient texts in Greece in 400 BCE and in the Roman *Natural History* written by Pliny, one of the first historians of Western civilization, in 77 CE. The word "bug" has its origins from *the* "bedbug," named thus in those ancient interactions with the bug that, thriving in warm and temperate climates of the Mediterranean, comes out at night to bite sleeping humanoids. It is believed that the bedbug evolved from a bat bug that coexisted with our ancestors when we were cave dwellers tens of thousands of years ago, and the DNA bears that out. Bedbugs, *Cimex lectularius*, translated from the Latin as "bug of the bed," are fully developed at ¼ inch (5-8mm). They work the late shift, active from 10 pm to 6 am, in the dark. They live in harborages in the cracks of floorboards, luggage, inside dresser drawers, upholstered furniture, electrical sockets. If there is a nook, if there is a cranny in an infested environment, there will be bedbugs or their larvae. They eat only once a week but can remain in an environment for 100-300 days without eating.

One major byproduct of mammalian exhalation is carbon dioxide. When we exhale, we expel the CO2 that is used by trees and plants in photosynthesis. Carbon dioxide also serves to alert the bedbug at night of human presence. When the bedbugs bite, they are attracted to a blood host, although they prefer humanoids to other mammals.

Once they have found you and a good spot to dine, they first inject you with a little anesthetic to keep you from awakening to the bite. Then they inject you with an anticoagulant to keep the blood flowing in optimum fashion while they are eating. The final act is to saw through your skin with mouthparts that cut through your tissue to find the right-sized blood vessel. The optimal blood vessel pressure will fill the bug's abdominal cavity with blood in three to five minutes.

Besides pest control, the natural predators for bedbugs are cockroaches, ants, some spiders, and mites. And then there is the primo predator, the masked bedbug hunter from the *Reduviidae* family, *Reduvius personatus*, so called "masked" because the nymph is hidden from their predators and prey by dust adhering to the sticky follicles that cover the 1/2–3/4 inch (10-20mm) body, effectively hiding a developing voracious bedbug hunter. The mature masked bedbug hunter can grow to almost an inch long.

Within a few days, the lab identified the bug that Marcy sent to University of Wisconsin Madison lab as a *Reduvius personatus*, the aforementioned masked bedbug hunter. The lab manager asked where the bug had come from because this particular bug was uncommon to Northern California, preferring hot and dry environments. The scientist/academic wanted to consult with his colleagues at UC Davis. Ultimately, he found there was no way to verify that the "assassin bug," another name for *Reduvius personatus*, came from Marcy's house or her room at the hotel, except by her word. The lab also identified the other bugs that Marcy had sent as a common centipede and a mite, both unremarkable bug residents of California.

Her lawyer told us that Marcy just wanted Liz back at home with her. We told him of our concerns. We described the required due process to him and set up an informal administrative hearing under California penal code section 597.1, in which we would describe our concerns and provide an opportunity to discuss conditions under which Liz might be returned to Marcy. Did he want to request such a hearing on her behalf? Marcy had already been given the paperwork to request the hearing but had not followed up. He would have to consult with his client.

Meanwhile Liz was doing well in our cat kennels and receiving lots of special attention from volunteers. In response to antibiotics, her blood values were returning to normal. It was the forensic veterinarian's opinion that Liz may have been given extra doses of a flea parasite preventative. Her kidney and liver enzymes had been abnormally high, as though fighting a mild poison. We were withholding that information from Marcy as the investigation continued.

The next day, Marcy's ex-husband called. He wanted to speak with not just anybody, but someone in charge. "My wife is disturbed," he said, "my wife is very disturbed." I told him right away that we had heard from her attorney and been advised that any further communication should go through him. "Fuck that," he said, "I want to talk to you."

Marcy had been spinning out of control for more than a month now, he said. He was very worried about her. She had had some manic and anxiety-related issues recently and this thing with the bugs had sent her into a major tailspin. He asked if there was any way he could use her cat, Liz, to lure Marcy into seeking the kind of mental health care she needed. I asked if Liz would be staying with him. He said no, that he couldn't keep Liz. I explained that we could not return her cat with the knowledge that Marcy may not be capable of caring for her in an appropriate way. I explained the concerns of the veterinarians, the investigating officer and the staff, as well as her option for a hearing.

Marcy's husband corroborated the weekend at the hotel. He said that she had been bitten by some kind of bugs while there, had an allergic reaction, and that she couldn't get it out of her head that the bugs had taken up residence in their home. Yes, he had moved out. What could be done? he wanted to know. He felt badly. So did we. The phone call ended amiably.

The next day, Marcy called and wanted to talk. We told her that we couldn't talk to her without her attorney. She said she was on her way over to our office, that she had fired her attorney. We called her attorney but he was in court, unavailable. We left a message with his assistant.

When Marcy arrived at our office an hour later, she was a wreck, pale, drawn and completely disheveled. She was wearing black capris spotted with bleach or some other cleaning agent, an aqua-colored cashmere sweater, a long trench coat, and spiky, very high heels. She was talking very fast and her face was red. She was a bundle of nerves and unsteady on her feet, with nonstop mile-a-minute talking: *My husband wants you to think I am crazy. I am not. I suffer from macular degeneration, this is a genetic thing, runs in the family, my eyesight is all blurry, I think maybe I am going crazy. I haven't eaten or slept in days. I need my cat. How is Liz? Can I see her? Did you see the results from UW lab? Means that there are bedbugs. I am not leaving without seeing my cat.*

She took off her coat in defiance, with the "I'm not leaving" protest. The sweater underneath was powdery or dusty with a fine white film over it, more splattered bleached-out spots, and holes the size of a dime that looked like acid burns. She pulled up the left arm sleeve of her sweater and showed us the bug inflammation on her forearms. She pulled out a magnifying glass from her purse and two more envelopes with what she called "specimens" in them, peering through the glass to look at the abrasions on her arm. Then holding the magnifying glass in her teeth, she pulled on the reddened and raw skin on the underside of her forearm, removing what looked like hair follicles, and placed them in a third envelope. There were about a dozen open wounds on her arm. She kicked off her shoes and asked one of us to take them outside. Now barefoot, she said the bugs were hiding between the soles of her shoes. She began crying. While I talked with her, other staff called the San Francisco Mental Health unit to see if we could get some help for her, in the form of an emergency intervention.

When the social workers arrived, we told them what we knew and they took about an hour to interview Marcy in private. They announced they were taking her to San Francisco General Hospital on a 5150 hold for evaluation. Marcy was livid. "I thought you were going to help me!" she screamed at us. The San Francisco Police Department came to help the mental health workers escort her to the hospital psych unit in a police car.

An insectary is a commercial biological factory where beneficial bugs are bred to help farmers, anglers, and even pest control specialists who address bug infestations. UC Davis entomologists thought that the *Reduvius personata*, the masked bedbug hunter sent to them by Marcy, was from an insectary in Georgia; they could tell from the bug's DNA. Apparently, there is an academic database for entomology research. Someone purchased masked hunters to fight off a bedbug infestation, the UC Davis lab chief believed, as they are not indigenous, do not live in California, and are very hard to find here. A call to the UC Riverside Center for Invasive Species Research led us to the Southern Associates Insectary outside Atlanta, GA. The nuisance-bug-versus-human work being done in the East was cutting edge. California insectarians, if there is such a term, were more interested in pests that impacted food crops, although an insectary in Redding was taking on houseflies, primarily for livestock but with implications for the mass market. The Atlanta insectary representative finally acknowledged that the masked bedbug hunter found in California was sold to a professional pest company in the Bay Area.

In the 1950s, bedbugs were not a problem in the United States due to the use of DDT in the 1940s. Apparently around 2008, a major bedbug resurgence came about. In New York City from 2004 to 2009, the numbers of bedbug complaints to the Health Department rose from 500 to 10,000. It was believed this was due to increased international travel, ignorance about bedbug habits and habitat, and the ban of DDT along with other powerful pesticides in the 1960s. (DDT was banned due to correlations with breast and pancreatic cancer.)

Heat of up to 125 degrees for four hours or temperatures below 0 degrees Fahrenheit for twelve hours will kill bedbugs. Cesium-137, a byproduct of uranium fission in nuclear power, will kill bedbugs. As a result of the Fukushima Daiichi Nuclear Power Plant meltdown in Japan, bedbugs have disappeared within a hundred miles of the plant. The CDC (Center for Disease Control) and many state public health agencies have attempted to alert the public to the reemerging problem of what has been referred to as the "bug-pire", a combination bug and vampire epidemic. There are not enough insectary masked bedbug hunters on the planet. Even though bedbugs do not carry disease to humanoids, they are considered a first-order nuisance. They freak people out. Thus in Georgia, it is good business to breed the assassin bug, the masked bedbug hunter.

~~~

The infestation obsession that Marcy exhibited was diagnosed as delusional. Because it was believed that she was not a danger to others or herself despite her skin picking, she was released after twenty-four hours on the mental health unit at SF General. Marcy was met by her sister and ex-husband and taken to the family home in Marin, because it was learned that the fire department had been at Marcy's house the day of the intervention. Marcy stubbornly continued to pursue her lawsuit against the ritzy hotel on Nob Hill. She could not attend the administrative hearing for Liz due to her health conditions. We found an ideal temporary situation for Liz until Marcy could recover sufficiently to attend a follow-up hearing.

About a month later, the last time I saw Marcy, she was slumped over in the driver's seat of her late-model black Lexus parked around the corner from the shelter. Her car had been in a couple of accidents: the front bumper ajar and falling off, good-sized dings, a headlight dangling. She was leaning way over the console and shifter. Her head was almost on the floor of the passenger seat. I thought she might be dead, I thought maybe suicide. There was no movement; I did a double-check to discern rising and falling ribs
~~~

to indicate she was still breathing. I thought to call 911 but didn't have my phone. Suddenly her head lifted slightly like she was underwater and there she was, squinting in the light, looking right through me, staring at the end of a pair of tweezers. She didn't even see me peering through the passenger-side window. The leather upholstery of the car was thrashed, with stuffing coming out and long razor-knife incisions running crisscross on both front seats and back. Clothing and multiple de-soled shoes lay akimbo on the floor within the car. Relieved that she was alive, I considered saying hello and asking how she was doing. Lacking the courage and the energy to engage, I walked away.

Months later, word got out that there was indeed a problem with bedbugs in some of San Francisco's best hotels.

Research shows there is a condition caused by a bedbug (or other bug) infestation called *delusional parasitosis*, the result of an infestation or the perception of a bedbug infestation, manifesting in what feels like bug scratching on or beneath skin. They call this sensation *formication.* (Yes, formication.) The sufferer usually looks for help from entomologists, veterinarians and pest control professionals, and their health condition remains undiagnosed. The result is Post Traumatic Stress Disorder (PTSD) with the associated anxiety, social isolation and withdrawal. The causes of formication can be drug induced (most commonly from cocaine or methamphetamine use), menopause, or even a real infestation, resulting in a pattern or fixation about crawling bugs that becomes delusional. In fact, the idea of being bugged is so anchored in our psyche and DNA that the mere suggestion of an infestation can induce the condition in others.

And finally, and somewhat frighteningly, the Morgellons Research Foundation, in cooperation with and documented by Kaiser Northern California, is seeing increasing numbers of cases of symptoms of an unnamed disease with simultaneous biting, crawling, or stinging sensations as a result of fibrous threads or black speck-like matter on or beneath the skin. They have used MRI technology to get pictures of these strands of organic matter under the skin. Other symptoms of this mysterious disease include changes in vision and delusions. Despite the evidence, there is skepticism in Western medicine that Morgellons is real.

If I learned one thing from Marcy, it is this: you never *really* know.

Outsider Ladies

Our house, Senior Rosa Parks Apartments, is need your assistance.

Please protect our cats which live on our garden. They not belong to anyone. No one care but us.

Our ladies begin feed, only on a daylight.

Since they, three cats live here, the mouse, which were so many on a house and on a garden, are disappear.

All the time was good, until came to our house the new resident, lady evil and cruel.

She doing chase against cats, urge her dog against cats.

Also, is very important: on a garden working two men. Every day on a garden. They working hard with machine. Cutting on a weeds, digging and pulling. Cleaning, such care, so thorough!

But the lady let her dog out on a garden. The work of men going to spoiled.

We don't know what apartments on this new resident but our security on a front door should know.

We asking you: please forbid her pursue our cats and doing dirty our garden by her dog.

On a street many owners own a dogs. They say because garden is special on a senior people, this lady must go on her dog to the street. Only to the street, not on a garden.

And, lastly, protect, please, cats of her dog because if she will drive out cats, the mouse will come back.

So, we will hope of your help.

Sincere yours,
The Ladies of a Rosa Parks

Golden Gate to Golden Gate

Golden Gate Ministry was home to a Baptist seminary of more than a hundred theology students in Mill Valley, California. The ministry carried the Word in a mission to share their Baptist *confession*, a declaration of organizing faith principles, throughout the United States and worldwide. "Some men and angels are predestinated [sic] to the praise of His glorious grace." Cody McGrath, a believer and a modern cowboy from New Mexico, was determined to carry the Good News and to do so on horseback, as a testament to and a test of his faith. He would ride from the foot of the Golden Gate Bridge on the far side of the San Francisco Bay to the Golden Gate at the eastern entrance to the City of Jerusalem. That was his one very ambitious goal.

As an iconic landmark, many are familiar with the Golden Gate Bridge of San Francisco, completed in 1937. It is the second longest main span suspension bridge in the United States, welcoming thousands of visitors to the West Coast annually. The Golden Gate

Bridge is never free from maintenance and is in perpetual process of repair or painting. The bridge marks the gateway or opening of the San Francisco Bay to the Pacific Ocean.

On the other hand, the Golden Gate of Jerusalem was built in the sixth century BCE, hundreds of years before the birth of Christ. It has been walled up since 810 AD. Frequently, Baptist doctrines state that the returning messiah will walk through that eastern Golden Gate with the promise of Armageddon and the Rapture for the Chosen. The saved will walk through the gate with Him and be delivered immediately to heaven.

Cody McGrath wanted to bring that news to folks he met while crossing the whole wide United (urban-suburban-rural) States. His plan was to ride his horse Molly, with a donkey in tow, from Golden Gate Bridge in San Francisco to the Golden Gate in Jerusalem. Cody had arranged to work on a steamer upon arrival in Baltimore in trade for his passage and that of his equine companions. His destination was Haifa in Israel, where Cody would resume his ministerial ride on land and continue his pilgrimage toward Jerusalem.

It was good news for the congregation in Mill Valley that Cody McGrath staged his departure on the Marin side of the Golden Gate Bridge, setting off at dawn on Easter morning mounted upon his bay filly and leading his gray donkey Blackjack, who was burdened with his camp gear for the long ride ahead.

For all who would witness this occasion offered in pious devotion and commitment to our lord and savior, Cody made it three miles, after about three or four hours, to within a block of the other San Francisco bridge, the Bay Bridge. Unconverted San Francisco police officers were called by someone among the few early-morning concerned witnesses. Upon hearing his story, SFPD placed Mr. McGrath into police custody and called the City's animal shelter for the safekeeping of Molly and old Blackjack while Cody was interviewed at the Southern Station by the police.

Until things could be straightened out with the official watch commander, the equines, Molly and Blackjack, walked eight blocks, clip-clopping in the bike lanes along not-so-busy-on-Easter-Sunday-morning Brannan Street, led by a City of Saint Francis shepherd, a San Francisco animal control officer. Like Joseph into Nazareth, they entered the back door of the Mission District animal shelter from the alley, through the cyclone-fenced gate, walking through the ubiquitous and incredulous homeless encampment at the back gate.

Inside, the kindly veterinarian, called in on a holiday, awaited the opportunity to begin health examinations on the saddled filly and pack donkey. She found that Molly had an abrasion on her right rear hock that needed treatment. Molly should not be ridden. Blackjack was more than twenty years old and should carry no more than 100 pounds, ideally less than that.

Within a couple of hours, the cowboy had been released from police custody with the caveat that the entourage could not traverse any public roadway, street, avenue, lane, yard or sidewalk or parking lot or park within the City of San Francisco. Good news or no good news. Cody arrived at the shelter, where he called his buddies at the seminary to solicit help from the congregation to bring a horse trailer to come and pick them up. It would take a couple of hours for those transport arrangements. Cody stretched out his long legs and fell asleep on the bench in the lobby of the shelter. Also on call, I arrived at the shelter when the good doctor was prepared to give the results of her health report.

The five of us—Molly, Blackjack, Cody, the vet and I—met in the garage of the animal shelter, where the gospel took over. Only two of us, the cowboy and the veterinarian, were believers. The representational Christian crosses needed no words. One of them was dainty gold at the vet's throat on a chain and the other was a thick silver Coptic design pinned on the lapel of Cody's long black oilcloth coat. These emblems seemed to commune with one another, even winking in the garage light reflected from above.

When the vet dropped the reins on Molly, the crosses brushed against one another as the doc and Cody both leaned down to pick up the leather strap attached to the halter. Their eyes met down there, so close to the earth, and the energy in the room shifted. Blood filled the vet's cheeks; she rushed to stand up and backed into Blackjack. The donkey whinnied and pushed his nose into her butt crack. Startled, she lurched forward, off balance. Cody was standing now and offered an arm to steady her. They were face to face, cross to cross, her cross settling lightly at the V of her scrub blouse, his head humbly bowed as the quivering passed between them. The crossroad, the intersection was heavy with potential romance, physical intimacy and a light-filled emotional significance. A dance was about to begin and the rhythm of the music was distant.

The atmosphere of the divine touched the DVM (Doctor of Veterinary Medicine) in a moment of eagerness on an Easter Sunday. Too soon, the other two cowboys from Petaluma were readying the horse trailer for loading, chatting away about how it was a good day to be doing God's work: bringing the Good News that Jesus Christ was born again on Easter, resurrected, risen, reunited with his Father in heaven after being condemned to death by crucifixion. Demeter and Persephone, if tuning into this story, may have recognized the borrowed theme.

So early on a wet, soggy Sunday morning before the kids woke up to search for the hen's prize, good news delivered the excitement of spring, a love spark, inexplicable, of whatever kind, between an inspired stranger and a woman whose devoted studiousness and mastery of linear thinking served her well in the pursuit of an advanced degree but resulted in profound loneliness, woe, a single life. For the time being, that sadness was relieved by the heat of the soft-spoken cowboy who had ridden the circuit of Wild West shows until he had a calling to bring the message by horseback.

Starting from the East Bay a couple of weeks later, Cody was back on the trail with Molly, riding her only occasionally but mostly walking. Last I heard he had traveled as far as Omaha, Nebraska. Cody and the good doctor stayed in email contact for a while. I don't know that he made it to the other Golden Gate. Or that they ever made a physical connection. But I sure hope so.

What I do remember, though, as he brought the good news of her desirability to our veterinarian, is that he also brought a message to me. When I jarred him from his slumber on the bench in the lobby, this handsome young cowboy named Cody woke up that Easter with a brilliant, warm smile for me, tired skeptic that I was. This genuine smile, the very friendliness of it, took me back to my child eyes as a devoted little Catholic girl in a trance over the rituals at Easter, when the church was lit by candlelight before the hour of resurrection announcing spring that very morning. Lifted up by the spirit, soul and passion of such a blossoming smile, I was, as I am now, once again reminded of an awed eight-year-old.

Can the good news of a budding smile really redeem? I believe it is so. That's my testament, my declaration in the space between Easter and Passover, as the sun moves closer and expanding daylight ignites growth in the northern hemisphere of our planet Earth.

Outsider: At Least Two Ways About It

A queer man named Michael had a dog named Pollock. There was a summer on Rhode Island where drugs, sex, and rock and roll were the order of the day. The drugs started the day. Rock and roll was the background music. Hard partying and prolific casual sex were the activities throughout the warm days and cool nights. One of those partying guys was Owen, another queer man who had a series of days, summers and winters, springs and falls full of partying in New York City, in Boston, on the Cape, and down the coast into Ashton and Raleigh. Owen graduated from Boston College, completed graduate studies in business and economics, and proceeded to blow his family inheritance on drugs, boyfriends and excess. He made it his business to party.

By the time Owen, thirty-six years old and down to his last $3,000, ran into Michael, well, ran into Michael's Toyota in a parking lot at a bar in P-Town (Providence, RI), Owen was a drug abuser, and sometimes sold drugs. He drove a black BMW convertible bearing evidence of multiple fender benders and late-night sideswipes.

The reputation that preceded him, however, concerned his dance moves. Owen had the rhythm, balance and skill to dance like no other. Turns out, Owen had once been a fierce competitor in the international ballroom dancing circuit in his twenties and had just missed placing as a finalist to represent the United States in the 1994 international event in Lisbon. When you could get him to talk about those days with friends, he would say that loss was his undoing. All who had witnessed it agreed: No one could dance like Owen. And when you partnered with Owen, you turned and twirled like never before, because he was that good. But Owen had few friends anymore, with his habit and a tendency to burn bridges. Owen had a mean streak as wide as the Pennsylvania turnpike and a temper that would shift like a big rig in the wind.

Michael, on the other hand, was significantly younger, a nice guy. Naive, sensitive and caring, he had become far too willing to have a couple of drinks to loosen up, to forget about the pain of a difficult upbringing and current caregiving. He had attended a small private college in upstate New York to become a nurse. Michael had a dog named Pollock who was his life and his companion through thick and thin. His two-year-old French bulldog sniffed and snorted, wheezed and waddled through his early but already very full life.

Owen and Michael met on a weekend outside that Providence bar in the middle of July, 2005. They had a monthlong raucous, raunchy and drug-induced sexual liaison, holed up in Michael's three-room apartment sixteen miles from Providence in Culbertson, Rhode Island. One morning when Owen left the apartment to get cigarettes, Michael, in overwhelm, exhaustion and fear, locked Owen out, leaving his stuff (mostly shorts and t-shirts) on the landing with a note. After an hour of Owen's banging on the door, the neighbors called the cops and Owen was threatened with arrest. Reluctantly, he left. Two days later, Owen broke into Michael's apartment and stole his laptop, his watch, his iPod, his grandfather's cufflinks and his dog, Pollock.

Michael was shocked. He didn't know what to do. He couldn't call the cops because he had an outstanding failure-to-appear warrant for his arrest. Twenty-four hours later he received the first of a series of taunting phone calls from Owen: "You won't open up the door to me, huh? Well, guess what? I've got it over you now, you sonofabitch...you'll never see your dog again." Michael cried and begged Owen to return his dog, but Owen laughed and hung up the phone.

Pollock, his baby, was gone!

Have you ever lost something that was an abstraction? Loss of sanity, loss of dignity, loss of meaning, loss of understanding, loss of innocence: all brought on by the loss of an influence in your life.

The grief was overwhelming as well as a very sobering event for Michael. You could even say it was a turning point. In order to file a police report, Michael had to clean up his act. He had to be able to walk into the Culbertson Police Department with credibility, which meant that Michael needed to go before the judge to clear his name from the drug-dealing charge. In his pain, Michael went back into his 12-step program. He parachuted into the war zone that was his upbringing once again. He ultimately began to deal with his poor life choices.

Some nine months later, Michael was still looking for Pollock. No word from Owen, whom he suspected was back in San Francisco. Michael tried the old phone number a dozen times a week: "This number has been disconnected and no longer in service."

Where is he? Where is Pollock? Please God, help me find my dog. Maybe I could fly out to San Francisco and find him? Maybe I could hire a detective to track him down? I've seen Owen's photo on a San Francisco gay porn website, maybe I could get him to contact me. Do I know anyone who knows anyone in San Francisco? Please, please, please...

"If you'd like to make a call, please hang up and dial the number."

In the end, what Michael did was to contact the NorCal French Bulldog Rescue group online. They had contacts in San Francisco, and when they heard Michael's story, they contacted the San Francisco local animal shelter and Michael did the same. Michael jumped through multiple hoops to prove his story. Finally, he was believed.

Without an address for Owen, there was little to be done. We, the authorities, would be "on the lookout." Posting on Craigslist, sending out photos of Pollock, and passing the word about a stolen French bulldog who may be living in San Francisco seemed woefully inadequate. But Michael would not give up.

And time passed.

Many months later, almost two years after the dog was taken from Rhode Island, Owen Singer walked into the San Francisco municipal animal shelter with a French bulldog he called Pollock. He wanted to purchase a license and apply for service dog status. The dog and Mr. Singer were recognized as parties to a very far-fetched investigation.

The police were called, Mr. Singer was detained, lawyers were contacted, supervisors were called, other phone calls were made; pleas became impassioned. It was no surprise that Owen had become very attached to Pollock. There was much pacing, anger, crying and gnashing of teeth. There was the matter of a police report filed by Michael Curtis from Rhode Island, a copy of which we had on file. Pollock was seized from Owen under protective custody.

Two days after the police were brought in, Pollock was on a flight to Boston, on his way home after a long and excellent adventure. There was one happy man at the baggage claim who had changed his life for the love of his dog.

Mr. Curtis declined to press charges against Mr. Singer. He only wanted his beloved Pollock back.

Michael sent us a photo of his reunion with his dog at Boston's Logan airport. He was driving a late-model BMW convertible now. He credited his improved life to Pollock.

A couple of years later, Owen came back to the shelter to apologize to us for his behavior during the conflict over ownership of Pollock. Due to Pollock's influence, Owen Singer had gotten his act together as well. He became a successful proprietor of a dog walker and pet-sitting business. Apparently, Pollock had altered the lives of both of his significant humans.

~

At the animal shelter in this large metropolitan area, we see this kind of tension between competing interests often. Trying not to judge but to witness and do the right thing, we say that we try to do the best *in the interest of the animals*. There is the law, there are rules, the question of rights and responsibilities. That is our job, which is often unpopular and certainly not simple. Reverence and transformation are the work of the animals, and the best we can do is advocate, give voice, be witness to all. Show up, pay attention.

Catenary* Cure

Who is Mother Teresa?

Why, Mother Teresa is the San Francisco savior of underage kittens, currently more than 200 ringworm (or ringworm-exposed) kittens in foster homes all over the Bay Area.

Mother Teresa, the missionary of the animal shelter, ever conscious of the lives she will save and the trials and tragedy of being born a feline in the midst of summer kitten season in urbanity. Mother Teresa and her network of apostles (volunteers) commit to kitty chaos for weeks and months to grow these critters in their own homes until they are old enough, weigh enough, are strong or well enough to be offered to the public or adopted by friends and family of the acolytes.

Mother Teresa is our unsung, un-beatified, indefatigable saint who facilitates these efforts; she is the hub, the *madame* of youthful at-risk cattery in San Francisco.

She rides in on a white horse (actually a gray Honda Odyssey more like a small whale), daily scanning the environs for orphan kittens or litters of kittens less than eight weeks old.

She will take bottle-feeders, eyes unopened, one day or ten days old; un-weaned, weaned, viable, feral, social or under-social, blind or deaf, cleft palates, no palates at all; those with herpes, calicivirus, coronavirus; emaciated, starved, underfed; with busted legs, eyes hanging out, de-breeded tails, birth defects, neurologic, prolapsed; suffering from ringworm, flat-, round- or tapeworm, as well as any other disease or mishap, known or unknown, to kittenkind. Whether rescued from the drive chain of an engine compartment, fallen from a fourth-story window or tire-marked by a beer truck, these kittens will have a chance.

Ever vigilant, Mother Teresa and/or her disciples are on watch for every carrier, cardboard box or soft duffel bag that comes through the front door. Then they reach behind the counter, into the wards, cages, kitchens or vet rooms, into air carriers, plastic and paper bags, and snatch those kittens from the precipice.

This, and this alone, is the work of our own single-minded Mother Teresa within the walls of the animal shelter.

And she is just one of the litany of saints who make up the volunteer corps at an animal shelter. There are the dog walkers, the dog trainers, dog socializers, dog advocates, dog rescuers and dog behaviorists. There are cat socializers and cat playtimes, play groups for both cats and dogs. There is TTouch™ therapy, aromatherapy, massage, Ayurvedic compounds; and there are psychics, diviners and mediums who will attempt to calm and communicate with animals in this San Francisco shelter.

Visible and invisible worlds! We sing their praises.

---

* Catenary (from Latin, fem. of *catenarius*, "of a chain," 1788) -the curve assumed by a cord of uniform density and cross section that is *perfectly flexible*...and that hangs freely from two fixed points (in this case, compassion and commitment).

Outside No More

Hilde was from Stuttgart. She fled the Nazis in 1937 when she was thirteen years old. Her parents sent her to the Ukraine with family friends, disguised as their daughter. She was lucky to get out; many of her family were not as fortunate. The Ukraine was the site of major pogroms in 1919–1920. And the Bolsheviks were not that welcoming to those fleeing the problems in Europe.

It would have been bad-mannered of me to ask for further details of her history during our meeting regarding her dog, Mikey.

Mikey was a pug, Hilde's pet. He was eleven years old. He had a tumor on his neck that oozed blood. He had been running down the avenues in the Outer Sunset District, at 26th and Moraga. He was wearing identification tags on a dirty green collar that traced him back to Hilde, who lived a couple of blocks away from where he was found. Relieved, the officer was able to quickly return him to her. Things went awry when Hilde refused to sign an agreement to have Mikey seen by a veterinarian for the bloody tumor on his neck.

Within a few minutes of their arising conflict, Hilde struck the officer multiple times with a clenched fist. Surprised, the officer covered her face with her hands and asked a neighbor to call paramedics. Hilde was taken to San Francisco General Hospital for a twenty-four-hour psych evaluation. Mikey came to the animal shelter.

When she came to our shelter offices the next day, Hilde showed me the bruises on her arms from being "manhandled" by the medics and orderlies at the hospital. "Who is going to pay for this?" she said to me, turning over her arms and thrusting her age-freckled, wrinkled yet strong, leathery arms toward me.

I told her we were meeting to discuss the situation with Mikey, her dog. But she was hard of hearing and couldn't hear me even when I spoke loudly. Hilde's friend and advocate Jose accompanied her. He quietly asked me to speak up and lean toward her right ear.

No matter what I said to her, how loudly or softly, I couldn't tell whether she heard me or not. I'll never know. In that long, intense meeting, her responses began and ended with: "Just give me my dog." No matter how many times I said, "I'd like to do just that...if you would have him seen by a veterinarian. You see, Mikey has more than just a bleeding wart; we are worried he has a collapsing trachea."

She refused, time after time. More than once, she stood up and pointed to her belly and said, "I have a tumor, too, and I will not be operated on. You do not hear me complaining, do you? My dog is fine. Just give me my dog."

When I asked if she had been interviewed by a social worker at the hospital, she shook her head. "I do not need any help."

"She refuses help from anyone except me. I am her only friend," Jose said, moving closer to her. He took her hand and said, "Hilde, let me take Mikey to the veterinarian. They'll let us take Mikey home if you let me take him to the veterinarian." Finally, she relented.

Now we needed to deal with the fees for Mikey's stay. "All my money is in stocks," she said, "illiquidity!" I almost laughed out loud.

Jose nodded. "She has no money," he said. The genteel middle-aged Latinx man was remarkable in contrast to Hilde, her angry sputtering hitting full throttle when she threw the paperwork at me, saying loudly, "I knew you were going to try and get my money. You are just like the Russians. The Nazis, even *they* were good to me. You and the Russians, ach! What has happened to this country when you extort money from an old woman?"

Jose told us that he helped Hilde buy groceries when he saw her once a week, for she did not have enough to get by on from her meager Social Security. He would call her for her list ahead of time, then drive his older model Peugeot to the Safeway at Stonestown. Often, she would forget to put bread and milk on her list. Hilde would not respond to anyone on the phone or at the front door anymore because she had been bothered and harassed by people trying to help her. Now she just picked up the receiver and listened; if it was Jose, she would talk to him but no one else. All her family and friends had died, he said, almost whispering, and her dog was all she had left.

Hilde couldn't accept that Mikey had been missing for more than an hour that day. She said her dog had been in the house. He couldn't have gotten out. Someone must have let him out, he was only gone for a minute, he scooted out the door under her unsteady feet. She claimed she had retrieved him quickly and returned indoors. Did she remember the officer coming to her door, asking her to have Mikey seen by a vet? "No, that didn't happen." Did she remember trying to remove Mikey from the animal control vehicle and being restrained by the police? "Who is going to pay for this?" she demanded, showing me her upturned reddened, black-and-blue forearms once again.

When I asked if she had been having problems with her memory, she responded angrily, "You are playing the age card. I knew this would come up sooner or later," and she laughed. She had this biting kind of laugh accompanied with a shake of the head and devilish smile. I note this leering kind of laugh from people who are angry in their gut, people who are usually demeaning, sarcastic, biting: this is another kind of aggressive animal, a trapped human being. Cornered like a dog in the backyard with no escape, throwing back their head, snarling and growling, lunging and defensive. They want the conversation over. It's all fear internalized, but they display this bravado. They are within the time they were powerless over a terrible experience; they are puffed up and big, bullying their way through.

I know people half her age who have trouble remembering, myself included. But I didn't respond because I knew better. This was serious non-remembering, cognitive-type confusion. Jose confirmed that he worried frequently that she would forget something on the stove, or wander around the neighborhood and not remember where she lived. That's why she didn't go out anymore. Jose also told me that the house was neat, not clean because she couldn't see, but she cleaned up after Mikey. Hilde refused to get glasses or a hearing device. "Too proud," he said.

Hilde stood up and said then, in a belligerent tone, "If you do not give me my dog, I will take a bottle of aspirin tonight. There is no reason to go on."

I made a decision to let Hilde take Mikey home with an agreement that Jose would take Mikey to the veterinarian within forty-eight hours...but also with the understanding that Mikey would probably not see a vet anytime soon, and that Hilde would probably not let him go outside again. Our shelter vet had given Mikey antibiotics and dressed his cauterized wound.

As Hilde's fear eased, she began to smile amicably and straightened the creases in her mauve flowered housedress. While we waited for Mikey's final paperwork, she beckoned me to move closer to tell me that the Feds ought to infuse the mortgage market with capital to stabilize the economy. "The culprit," she said, "was those damn credit default swaps." She went on, "Those people who bet in favor of others' losses ought to be censored and barred from Wall Street, if you ask me..." she trailed off.

Then suddenly, angrily, "Just give me my dog!" As she walked out the door with her little dog Mikey in tow, she muttered, "Just like the Russians..."

~

Beginning in 1951, Hilde Ingersol had worked thirty years for the federal government. I learned she had been a translator and interpreter for the Federal Reserve Bank in the Chicago branch for many years. I might have paid closer attention to her financial advice.

~

Later that week we checked in with Jose. He said Hilde had refused to let him take Mikey to the veterinarian. Mikey was eating, and Jose thought Mikey seemed to be doing better. Last time he went to the store, the shopping list included diapers. He wasn't sure if they were for Hilde or for Mikey.

Weeks later, Jose called us to report that Hilde's dog Mikey had passed and could be found on her front porch. When we arrived, Hilde would not open the door or talk to the officers. We left a notice to say we needed to check on her and discuss Mikey's death.

Adult Protective Services, social workers, even Jose could not get her to open the door. Eventually, together we were able to acquire a court order for a welfare check. Hilde was found in her bedroom, dead for a few days, with a bottle of aspirin on the bedside table.

~

I pause here, trying to make sense of this story, some moral or meaning beyond the facticity and challenge of the telling. Thoughts sink to the bottom like sediment in a cup of water taken from the creek of life, rushing by from chaos upstream.

- In this country, you have the freedom to die as you like, in isolation if you choose.
- Other living creatures may not have the freedom to do so because they do not have cognition, moral standing or power. They have a protectorate and maybe an advocate.
- In this country, you can be the author of your misery.
- In some other countries, those in power or the governments of those countries may choose to manufacture the misery for you.
- The United States does a fair share of misery creation for people within and without.
- Intervention is a preemptive strike and is just like fortune telling.

- No one knows the future.
- *Yir'Ah* in Hebrew means "awe."
- A powerful feeling of beauty can be awe-inspiring.
- A powerful feeling of danger can be awe-inspiring.
- A powerful feeling of reverence can be awe-inpiring.
- Beauty, danger and reverence are worth pursuing.
- When the awe-inspired anchors itself in our unconscious, those influences and perceptions go far beyond the context.
- "Truthiness," the 2008 word of the year, is some thing one claims to know from the gut without regard to evidence, logic, intellectual examination or facts. This, we are told, is dangerous. Truthiness becomes an obstacle to an honest and clear voice. This in 2008, in the midst of the banking meltdown in the United States and internationally. This, within the misery of all that followed, the financial misconduct of greedy financial manipulators and their algorithms.
- *Yoffi* in Hebrew means "hoorah!" or "bravo!"
- "*Yoffi Yir'Ah*," I say today, fenced in by the Book of Life. Hooray for awe!

Munchausen Maybe

Schlep, schtick, spiel.

This week was full of "shushing" as I schlepped thoughts to and fro, forward and back: I picked up the schtick when it's my turn to talk, my spiel fast pitch; I batter-chattered to the staff, the media on the phone, the volunteer who wanted an interview on my quirky work, the report due to the director, the new building costs.

What prepared you for your work? the interviewer wanted to know. I said, *My life up to that point and my life up to this point. I am privileged to be involved in work that has a point and makes a point.* Work that encourages self-reflection, personal growth and poetry...I don't say that. I think it later.

A process for figuring out how to ask the right questions:

Is today the last day...

of the sale

to move out

of the playoffs

of chemo
of our vacation
to take advantage of the offer
before the end of the world for the kitten with an exposed cranium

The only thing more fleeting than summer...
is a good laugh
is the pink sunrise
is the melody of a musical phrase
is the sight of a raptor with a mouse in her talons
is the bloom of the lavender rose
is a night of uninterrupted sleep
is that insight into my behavior over dinner last Wednesday
is my understanding of Nietzsche
is the life of my little dog, Mini

Wendy Steel: hipster-ish woman in her thirties, husky, porcelain complexion, crimson lipstick painting a thin mouth in an exaggerated arch under wide nostrils. Her eyebrows must be tattooed because they are Joan Crawford perfect. Thick black-rimmed eyeglasses accented bright, Key West-blue, Florida-Atlantic eyes. Wendy wore brightly colored patterned blouses atop black tights, her jet-black hair cut Cleopatra style. She was thick around the waist, big busted with no hips or butt on top of skinny legs. Wendy used brightly patterned fashion to distract from her disproportionate torso, and of course, it worked.

Her cat, named JayJay, was a bright orange and white two-year-old neutered male. He had been brought to the vet five times in two years with blunt trauma to various parts of his body: the right front leg, the left rear leg, rib, nose, skull. He now wore an apparatus on his back leg to help him to walk. Veterinary bills were more than $13,000 for various procedures to correct injuries for an extremely accident-prone cat. And this time, it was all too strange.

Wendy had met her boyfriend at San Francisco General Hospital, when he was a security guard. Also in his thirties, Orlando was a husky, warm kind of guy with an easy demeanor who talked nonstop. He played Santa Claus when he returned to Manila to visit family during winter holidays. A student at DeVries Institute learning to be a copier technician, Orlando had been unemployed and picking up odd jobs for eighteen months. He was almost done with school. His cat Sally was an average-sized brown and black tiger with big yellow tiger eyes.

JayJay and Sally had lived with Wendy and Orlando since they had moved in together more than two years ago. The couple were in an apartment on the edge of Lower Haight in a changing neighborhood. They believed that JayJay and Sally were roughhousing while they were left alone at home. Recently, Wendy returned from her graveyard shift at General as a radiology technician to find the apartment a wreck and JayJay injured once again. She woke Orlando to report the latest. *Not again!* JayJay must be getting hurt in the excitement of the game, the battle between the felines, the competition, the chase. Sally was admonished and JayJay was packed up to go to the emergency veterinarian.

Occasionally, when exuberant play was witnessed by the humans, the cats were given time-outs and separated if they became too raucous in the house. Once Wendy and Orlando came into the kitchen and saw the cats flying through the air, jumping up and then sliding across the kitchen floor. And apparently, it was believed, when unsupervised, the cats became overly enthusiastic in their play. The result was that JayJay was hurt, two times, three times, six times now.

The veterinarians and the investigating officer considered other possibilities. The litany of injuries and the type of consistent blunt trauma to JayJay indicated that something else may have been going on. The fact that Orlando was at home and asleep during the latest incident made some difference. No one else came into the home. Wendy and Orlando were both out of the house for eight to ten hours most days.

The investigating officer presented her case. The couple was separated and interviewed, a process of questions. Questions, questions; and more questions.

To Wendy: Does your boyfriend lose his temper?

Is Orlando depressed since losing his job? What happens when you have a disagreement? Wasn't he arrested in a dispute with an ex a couple of years ago? Has he ever hit you?

No, no, no! Orlando would never hurt me or JayJay. He is very mild-mannered, he loves the cat, he loves me, he would never do anything to hurt the cats. His teenage daughter and her mother were physically fighting and he stepped between them. It was a wrongful arrest of a brown-skinned man.

Wendy, listen, the facts fit the profile of possible domestic abuse.

To Orlando: What happens when Wendy loses her temper? How do you discipline the cats? How does Wendy discipline the cats? Is Wendy depressed? Is she needy? Has she ever hit you?

I just ignore her, she just gets worked up, she has done everything to prevent further injuries to JayJay. The cats are separated when we are out of the house, JayJay goes into the bathroom. To discipline, I just stop playing with them. She uses a newspaper and a water spray bottle, or gives them a time-out.

No, no, no, we are very happy together. We are thinking of getting married next year.

Orlando, listen, the facts fit the profile of Munchausen Syndrome by Proxy*.

What's that?

A person acts as if they are caretaking a dependent individual when in fact, in secret, in private, they are actually harming the individual. They do this in order to bring attention to themselves, to create drama, to break a cycle of boredom.

Impossible. Wendy would never hurt her cat.

Wendy and Orlando and Officer Woods and me: Together again around a large laminate conference table in my office, we agreed that there was something going on to cause JayJay's injuries. Was there any explanation we had not explored?

"Well..." Orlando said slowly, "you are going to think this is crazy...there is the fact that the apartment is haunted. We have, each of us, on separate occasions and together, seen spirits in the apartment. Our names have been called in the voice of the other in the absence of the other. We have felt the chill of a shadowy presence. Wendy and I have been thinking about moving."

Wendy was really crying now. "It does sound crazy."

Me: "In the meantime, I do not think it is safe for JayJay to return to your home. Will you consider allowing us to rehome him with another family?"

Wendy was still crying. "Absolutely not," said Orlando, "that would break Wendy's heart." Orlando reached over to console Wendy, who said, through tears, dabbing her eyes, "Yes, I think that would be a good idea."

Was it face saving, was it grace, a supernatural mystery, a way out? Or maybe an illogical syllogism? Aristotle defined syllogism in *Prior Analytics* as "a discourse in which certain things which are supposed, then result in something different." In practical usage, a syllogism is an inference from at least two other factual statements, the basis of inductive reasoning in problem solving. You decide which two statements are the facts, what is induced or inferred, and whether the solution follows the factual circumstances. Ask more questions and you might come up with a hypothesis, then you'll be in the realm of deductive reasoning.

~~~

Humanoids are good at problem solving. Physicists will tell you that life is one big problem that can be solved by mathematical equations. I personally don't believe it, nor did Kurt Gödel (mathematician and philosopher). The point is...and we return to this point often...the result is many, many more questions than answers. One active principle: live with the mystery as long as you can, until some being gets hurt... and some questions abduct all reason, all logic, all thinking. Do the next right thing.

Schlep, schtick, spiel...maybe all that shushing could sing a lullaby to my searching mind.

---

*Munchausen Syndrome by Proxy is also known as Factitious Disorder Imposed on Another (FDIA)
~~~

Particular Outsider

In the center of "other" is "the" (tee, aitch, ee), sometimes pronounced "thee" but only when used in front of words beginning with a vowel. "The" and "thee" are the most commonly used words in the English language. "The" is an article, a definite article referring to a specific thing. While "an" and "a" are indefinite articles, their noun not yet a particular one. Thus, a pinch of an "an," a cup of "other,"—add "outsider" and you have soup.

In this case, Stanley was "a" specific individual who had in his environment many, many specific articles and numerous indefinite ones. The collection did not begin with him but was carried on by him, a legacy of articles, mostly nouns.

Stanley had arrived at the gate of advancing middle age in poor shape. In his late fifties, he was of a rather stocky build with a ruddy complexion; his ears were extra large, bluish in color, and stuck out from a small skull heavy with unkempt, thick, predominantly gray hair and one huge black eyebrow across his forehead. He was painfully polite, referring to all in a formal way, using miss and mister and ma'am in a deep, atonal, complaining voice. His facial expression was frequently plain misery and quite sad appearing. His brown eyes were filmed and yellowish-blue, rheumy, accented by folds of skin under his eyes and thickening eyelids, making eye contact with him heavy and burdensome, reflecting a real chore.

When I first met Stanley, he wore soiled gray wool slacks with a pin-striped shirt, a blue and maroon argyle sweater and scuffed wingtips. The London Fog overcoat he wore to the meeting missed buttons on the double lapel and belt.

He had graduated with honors from Boalt Hall, the law program at Berkeley in the early 1970s. Stanley was among the top of his class. He found court in front of an omniscient black robe anxiety-provoking and left active litigation to pursue work in real estate law, mostly crunching numbers. He was very good at it.

Over the years, he slid in and out of despair, in and out of trial antidepressant SSRIs (selective serotonin reuptake inhibitors) and the resultant occasional stints in SROs (single resident occupancy hotels) frequently occupied by homeless people. He never married or found a mate, and said he hadn't much use for his own bed or even a couch except to watch TV. About fifteen years before our meeting, he had moved back home to his biological family's residence in the Sunset District, a middle-class neighborhood in San Francisco, where he and his dogs shared their lives.

His mother had found her refuge in a nursing home in Pacifica a few years prior with some form of dementia. Since that event, Stanley lived alone at the family home in the center of chaos both physical and mental, which became increasingly overwhelming for him. To deal with social isolation, Stanley acquired pet-quality German shepherd dogs from a breeder for whom he did part-time work in the East Bay. The canines depended on him, would never leave him. They would love him unconditionally. They would create a home together. They needed him. He needed them.

Late in the calendar year before our introduction, Stanley was hospitalized in an emergency intervention and placed on suicide watch. At the suggestion of a neighbor who knew there were dogs in the house, the police inspected his residence and found eight dogs (seven German shepherds and one Alaskan malamute), and conditions in his home that were beyond description. The house on Noriega had fallen into complete and utter squalor through neglect, hoarding, and family members' inability to part with refuse. This was the result of many years of everyday collecting and shopping initiated by his mother, dating from the death of Stanley's father in 1991 or earlier, and was exacerbated by Stanley's own hoarding and his numbing depression.

Plaster from the ceiling in the living room had fallen down, and rooms throughout the house were impassable without sinking into a spongy underlayment two feet deep of unfathomable, impenetrable, unidentifiable piled-up garbage. A good portion of the living room, hallway and den on the first floor was cave-like, completely blocked with a mountain of stuff (indefinite articles) including clothing, newspaper, books, even furniture; that is, couches, chairs, mattresses, and pillows that were not just ripped but broken, gutted, shredded and completely deconstructed. Wallpaper peeled in large sections from corners of every room of the three-bedroom, two-bath residence. Paintings on the walls were warped from the dampness, which appeared to be a combination of animal urine and leaking roof. All the hardware on the doors and windows, furniture drawer handles and door knobs were rusted. The remains of a sectional couch and overstuffed chairs were upside down on the peak of mountainous debris in the center of the living room.

The blinds were closed to the outside world and darkly caked with accumulated fly dirt, oily and greasy. They hung askew, just barely keeping the outside world from breaking through, or otherwise preventing the accumulated matter within these rooms from bursting out into the street beyond. The bedrooms and beds were piled high with composting, mildewing fabric, damp and rank, decomposing cotton and denim and polyester clothing, jeans and suit jackets and socks. Bath and kitchen paths were carved out in rocky, uneven trails to each inoperative sink and bowl, those rooms also packed to the ceiling with more newspaper, books, magazines, and other compacted objects. Space drowned by inertia, the inability to discard that which is of no use, no longer of value, and yet which continues to grow, multiply, replicate and consume space.

The story goes, as recounted in that first meeting, that Stanley became more disoriented and depressed after his mother left the home and consequently he neglected his beloved dogs: Natasha, Teddy, Thor, Tommy, Sue, Billie, Ceres and Sam. He banished them to the ground-floor garage, into pilings of specific things (nouns all): saws and coffeepots and pizza makers, concrete mix, galoshes and kitchenware, four different late-model scooters, a vintage Lincoln Town Car that had belonged to his father and a '66 red Ford Mustang belonging to his mother. New stuff was still in boxes and plastic packages, and there was an extensive collection of all sizes and shapes of Tupperware, old rusty jars of nails, hasps, bolts and washers. The dogs created pathways through the piles in the garage, buckling the auto engine hoods in their romps about the area, scratching and circling in the debris in which they slept.

Stanley spent little time in their company anymore—neither the animate nor the inanimate down in the garage. Under this regime, the dogs became frantic and undersocialized, reverting to feral beings: wild, pushing and pulling, nudging and throwing themselves toward him when Stanley tried to interact or feed them, scratching and biting, tearing at his pantlegs. Consequently, Stanley avoided mealtime.

Recently, he had began using a long stick to open the back door from above to let them out in the yard, and eventually he left the door to the yard open at all times. The garage stairway became stacked with extra stuff flooding from above, impossible to navigate without a sled or a set of ropes and pulleys.

Stanley agreed to give up five of his eight dogs to begin to deal with the crisis of his chaotic living conditions. An area toward the back of the garage on the ground floor had been cleaned up for the dogs. He promised to follow the timeline of the Code Enforcement Unit that was now involved due to public health and safety concerns about the massive cleanup necessary at his residence. Dogs Sue, Billie and Sam would be seen regularly by an APS (Adult Protective Services) caseworker who would inform us at the shelter if Stanley was not abiding by the signed agreement. Neighbors said they would help monitor the situation.

~~~

And then came the spring day a few months later when Stanley took an overdose of his medication, too many sleeping pills washed down with vodka, the door upstairs left ajar. The three still-neglected dogs invaded the upstairs, looking for food perhaps, exploring the only marginally improved and still-torn-apart place. As Stanley lay unconscious on a pile of rubble in the dining room, the dogs began to lick and then, punc-
~~~

tuating their severed domestic environment, began to devour his face. They chewed off the lobe of one ear and nipped at his eyebrow; they took a chunk of his chin and had begun ripping at his nose when he awakened and called 911. In the ruckus of that day, the blinds on the picture window facing the street fell down. The crusty blinds were open for the detritus hurled about the room to become the subject of neighborhood curiosity, alarm and photography.

If it was not enough that he was severely depressed, Stanley's ultimate humiliation was being mauled by beloved companion dogs who, in accordance with their natures, proceeded to predate the departed before the departed was dead.

Through the intervention of "thee" authorities, "the" victim was rescued and "the" dogs escaped their dungeon before resorting to cannibalizing each other. For Stanley, it may have been too late to resurrect his clogged life, to recognize impossible denial and reduce his illusive, maladaptive illness toward some type of orderly behavior. Stanley's redemption would take resources beyond those available to him, through those who knew him or had come to know him, and even through the strangers whose lives intersected his at this junction. It was pitiable. It was pitiful. A past participle.

The animals' lives were spared. In a town that could ill afford pity in those days following the 2008 recession, somehow it was easier to forgive the *canid* than help the *hominid*. The dogs were placed in foster homes, eventually to be permanently adopted. There was reasonable belief they would forget their tragic beginnings and go on to live productive dog lives.

Similarly, with our own dogs, we are able to silence memory, forget the transgressions, excuse the behavior as consistent with their dog nature. Forgetfulness allows the illusion that teleology and civilization move forward. At least, that is the proposition.

But what of the broken man, the complexity of whom is inscrutable, consumed by consumption? The city would name a public guardian, charge him, and commit Stanley into the care of a caseworker. Whose responsibility, the lost souls in the midst of life by ordeal? Stanley needed a public guardian angel, a savior of lost causes, someone to wash his feet with her hair: Mary, Ursula, Divine Mother. Is there no limit to the manifestations of pain? There was no one for Stanley. No miracle worker or superman or long lost relative nor friendly church lady at the ready.

⁂

Pathetic is a term from the Greek *pathos*, meaning a suffering feeling. I suggest this is a pathetic effort to reveal language as inept; that grammar and rhetoric are at each end parentheses to this story, that this discourse is generated in a collection of adverbs, adjectives and prepositions, nouns too numerous and a lack of verbs, contributing to an abstract experience. I bring no single definite or indefinite article to the action except in telling the sad tale of inaction.

All of it, yes, *all* of it, eventually to be discarded, unless the metaphor explodes within our consumer (consumptive) society and inevitably leads to the extinction of human life on Earth. The only real question is "How many other animal and plant species have we taken, and will we take, with us?"

Stand-Up, Stand Down

Performer, comic, writer she was. Her stage name was Ruth Piper. When we first met, she made a joke about being the Pied Piper. I wasn't sure how to take that comment. Her mind was very sharp in some ways and in other ways, not so. But there was no ambiguity about her blind spot: her body was a mess. She smelled like ammonia. Ruth did not know how Ruth smelled, could not smell her Ruth-self. Like when you can't smell your close environment, or you sniff your own flatulence and it doesn't smell so bad. Like people who smoke or a house that smells like cat poop, Ruth had acclimated to her own scent.

She brought her dog named Baby Doll to the shelter to be groomed and sat in the crowded lobby just before the daily 11 am opening. She tried to engage me in a conversation about my nickname as I rushed by the green bench where she sat. But I was on a mission, off to visit the marmoset that was headed to a sanctuary near Austin. Or was it the five roosters confiscated from a breeder on their way to the Philippines? Some animal needed to go somewhere. This mammal of myself, in a metaphoric kind of way, was focused on facilitating transport, otherwise known as getting-them-there.

And yet there she was, seen from the corner of my distracted eye. And I couldn't do it; she was rambling about some esoteric subject in art history and I couldn't accept the polite urge to stay there with her. I tried to release myself from guilt by convincing myself that I had too much to do, as I avoided passing her deteriorating body and slumped spirit by going up and down the backstairs.

Ruth was in her late fifties, tallish at 5'10" or so, frail and thin. Her clothes were scraggly: dark-colored blouse with a vintage '70s oversized collar and shoulder pads and green khaki pants with yellowed athletic socks and running shoes. She told me one day that she had never worn a t-shirt. She had a theory about people who wear t-shirts. *It couldn't be "just not her style,"* I thought. In my imagination, it was just possible that she was right; that her wearing a t-shirt, even one with sequins and flamingos, embroidered and expensive, would take her appearance down another notch.

She had a thick red skin tone and thin, straight, greasy reddish-brown hair in a cut to just below her shoulders, with bangs in her eyes. Ruth had a low-pitched voice, throaty, like it was emerging from a cavern behind her soft palate before vocal vibrations rushed to freedom into the light through her teeth. There was energy held on the roof of her mouth, above her sinuses, above it all, as she lifted her chin and pursed her lips, resulting in a feeling that I was audience, in the presence of royalty, when she said she must help us understand that she had been victimized by her landlord and the contractors who were paid to help her. It was in Ruth's voice, the way she held her head, and her physical presentation from the neck up; she was a superior person, if in head and voice only. But in fact, Ruth was a wreck; the drawbridge was up, the moat was wide, and she was so diminished that the crumbling castle of her life was distorted, becoming ghostly.

Could it be that her senses were compromised? Her sense of self, her smell, the contradictions of her voice, and now her sight. She could not see herself. (How to make sense of the senselessness of her situation?) Was it my obligation or responsibility as a fellow human being to help her, or should I at least have asked if she needed some help? And what would "help" mean? *No, you cannot move in with me. No, you must begin to grapple with reality, with your problems.* What if she could *not* grapple with her problems, as it certainly appeared? She was like a person with dementia standing before me naked, asking me to try to remember how they lost their clothes. And did I have something they could wear? As long as it wasn't a t-shirt, and best if it was something from the '70s.

To complete a welfare check, we arrived at her apartment near Golden Gate Park. Her buzzer didn't work, so it wasn't easy to get inside. She left the key taped under the box so we could open the front door, though neighbors warned against it. Ruth had lived in her apartment for more than fifteen years, rent control protected.

The inside of her home was almost as much of a wreck as her body. Her bed was covered with pillows, all puffy and flowery in orange and pea green heavy upholstery fabric. Did I say, "The room smells like urine?" One dog peed, the other defecated on the rug while we were there. She needed an advocate but would not get help unless she requested it.

Ruth Piper, suffering from fibromyalgia, the ex- performer/comedienne who wrote reams about the meaning of nicknames and their origins and chronicled the psychology of people who reject their God-given name in favor of a different or shortened "nick" name.

Three dogs: We were supposed to limit our worry to just this issue. Three little Pomeranian dogs wandered the apartment, two males and a female, suspicious and hopeful at the same time. Withdrawing from her and in need of major grooming, with fecal matter stuck to their fur and cleaning needed around the anal glands. *Poor thing.* I didn't know if I meant Ruth or Baby Girl, the oldest of her dogs, who never left the flat.

Soon after our home visit, I hoped Ruth had not called and left long-winded, affect-laden messages on my voicemail, but she had. The upside: she announced that she would no longer board dogs at her house for a living, for financial gain. She recognized this decision would greatly impact her finances, as she lived with limited income.

Maybe we would have to get Adult Protective Services involved.

I thought it was the dogs who were not house-trained and soon realized that it was the human animal who was having problems getting to the toilet. If you do not have an advocate, what do you do? As your physical and mental health diminishes and you become isolated and ashamed, the ability to traverse the landscape of urban life in the United States in the twenty-first century seems impossible. And yet people trudge along, doing the best they can, berating the dogs, the landlord, the workmen, the president if they have to; creating a noisy diversion in art history and nicknames, dredging up esoteric philosophical theories and memories of a personal best, like that comic performance at Slim's in the summer of 1974.

After Ruth died a year or so later from complications of her disease, a friend of hers delivered an envelope from her to my office. It contained a photograph of Ruth's in-house cremation display. This was a sculptural diorama in an eighteen-inch plexiglass cube that held plastic statues of Dracula, Frankenstein and Pee-Wee Herman, and was draped with a bright red bow. The handwritten note on the back of the photo read: "Please keep so everyone sees, then give to Deputy

Kat—a little boy's niche with wind-up toys, note the two vases on either side's niche. There's a first-floor room to prepare your flowers. It's a rich experience. A columbarium."

I took her note as an indication that her death was perhaps premeditated, or at least she knew the likely outcome of her disintegrating health. And I kept the note because the word *columbarium* was interesting to me. I kept it because it was an apparent invitation to remember her. I kept it to create my own imaginative crypt, catacomb or burial display.

The Silence of the Beast

This is one of the stories that haunts me in those pre-dawn moments before waking. These stories wail at me to find voice...however cracked and addled.

Convicted child molester Randy Knight, thirty-eight years old, took his own life in the San Francisco County Jail two days after he was arrested for animal abuse. There was no word from his ex-wife. His chosen family of friends, if there were any, may have decided it was too dangerous to come forward because of the nature of his trouble. Of Randy's family of origin, only his older sister from the East Coast contacted us afterwards. She wanted to know if we could meet and talk, if she could see the evidence of Randy's crimes against animals, to understand the reason for his arrest. She came into town to identify his body in the morgue, to collect his possessions and clean up the house where he lived. Because we had served a search warrant on his residence before his death, Randy's sister asked if we had any "personal effects."

It seemed ludicrous that she would be asking for personal effects when her brother had been making molds, casting and selling large-sized dildoes made in soft, hard and firm plastic in various bright fluorescent colors, fashioned after animal genitalia. Apparently, our man had an odd sense of humor.

Understandably, his sister did not, at least at this point. She was upset and angry. "What happened?" she wanted to know. She told us her brother was different; he was a free thinker, a radical, ahead of his time. He'd researched sexual expressions in modernity and traveled widely in Europe and the Netherlands until he married in the 1990s. He had kids and a master's degree in human sexuality from a big-name university. He was supposed to thrive in the Bay Area. She did more talking than we did. I'm sorry to say we probably didn't provide much solace to Randy's sister.

During the execution of the search warrant, we found some of the dildoes packaged in boxes, some still in the molds, some just lying about, some in plastic bags with labels. There were horse penises in pink, goat penises in bright green, flesh-colored donkey penises, a whole little factory of rubber animal genitalia in a garage in the Sunset District of San Francisco. In gathering the evidence, samples of each species had to be collected. Identifying each and distinguishing a goat dildo from a sheep dildo was interesting, if not challenging. The horse dildo was not difficult. There were choices of dildo stiffness, from rigid A to B or C. We found sales receipts indicating that Randy sold these sex toys to leather shops on Folsom Street. Some were mailed out of town.

The modest stucco house with a street level garage and the main residence upstairs was located in a changing neighborhood of university students, young families and elderly people, both Asian and Anglo. Situated a couple blocks from the beach, houses in this Ocean Beach neighborhood were attractive to college kids who were surfers, a few small-time cannabis and meth dealers and their followers, families in transition, and couples with small children breaking into a tough real estate market while counting on neighborhood gentrification.

~~~

In the row after row of soft-structure houses on 26th Avenue, Miriam, the elderly homeowner, was biding her time until (she worried) she could no longer live on her own. The exterior paint was faded and peeling and a big wrought iron security gate crossed the entrance. The buzzer was broken, the gate lock inoperative. A big picture window with heavy faded drapes tightly drawn loomed above the garage facing east, toward the street.

On a clear sunny morning in the middle of the week, the warrant was served in Randy's name to Miriam. The house belonged to her clear and free, and she rented the ground floor room downstairs off the garage to Randy to help pay taxes. She had no idea! Like Danny
~~~

Thomas, she said, she was Lebanese, a second-generation immigrant, born in San Francisco. Dusty Christian memorabilia were everywhere in her flat. Miriam was the last surviving member of her family; her brothers were gone, one killed in WWII and her kid brother, who used to take care of her and her mom, dead of cancer at sixty in 1990. When her mother became sedentary in old age, Miriam took care of her until she died in 1995. Miriam had retired as a bookkeeper for the local Baptist church a couple of years earlier, and ownership of her house would transfer to the church when she died. She was frugal, squeaking by on Social Security and her meager savings. The roof on the house was leaking, but the church had found a donor to help repair that about a year ago. Her old-fashioned TV only got three channels with a flimsy inside antenna, the screen blurry, with continuous audio static. When she could hear the sound, Miriam liked to listen to *Wheel of Fortune*. Could I look at it before I left to see if I could get a clearer picture, better sound, maybe?

The church helped Miriam find Randy as a boarder. He was a nice young man, she said. He helped Miriam with groceries and some household chores. Randy only came upstairs occasionally to cook a meal, eating out frequently or bringing home take-out food. Miriam's kitchen revealed an oily yellow scum around the edges of cabinets and countertops, marked by sticky dirt and grime. Everything in the place, from faucets to silverware to the teapot on the sink, looked grungy and felt tacky. Thick, dark spectacles sitting heavily on her nose, Miriam proclaimed that her vision wasn't the greatest any more.

Randy's small bedroom and bath within the garage walls toward the back of the building had been built in the 1970s for Miriam's younger brother, when he moved back in the family home after receiving a cancer diagnosis. The bed was crammed into the room, which had just a tiny window looking out toward the tall weeds in the backyard. Randy's manufacturing operation took place at the street end of the garage, which was generous in comparison with his living quarters. A half dozen 55-gallon drums of smooth cast resin and polymer/rubber products were assembled in an aisle on the concrete floor, along with a large wooden workbench covered with plastic molds and casting tools. Aerosol cans lined the back of the workbench. A standard card table with a metal folding chair sat at the stairway with paperwork, a receipt book and a recipe file box on top. Different sizes of silicon and hard plastic molds were scattered about the room. An old gray couch against the back wall interrupted the incongruous workshop. The dildoes were an obvious hint of the unusual misconduct we were soon to expose in this bizarre setting.

Upstairs in Miriam's place, at the dining room table in a little alcove, the vice inspector from the SFPD and I interviewed Randy. The stunned and scared suspect was handcuffed to a dining room chair. The inspector asked questions about who Randy might be dating these days. "Who ya goin' out with, Randy? Ya seein' anybody?" And without giving him a chance to answer, "A guy, a gal…how about a dog?" Like a peal of thunder, I felt the overwhelming heaviness of this situation.

The interrogation at that dark walnut table went on for more than an hour without much result except that Randy became more afraid and more withdrawn, inanimate and dull. He had an odd plastic device clipped to his belt, a child's toy with a fading image of Captain Kirk (of Star Trek) and a pinpoint flashing red light on the top. He told us that a kid he had befriended down the block gave it to him.

Randy's rap sheet noted charges of child sexual abuse. Stung by his reference to the neighborhood child, I asked him directly about his sexual attraction to dogs. Bizarre photographs of dog genitalia had begun the investigation in the first place. Offhandedly, he told me that he was very, very careful with animals, not to take advantage of them, that is. Randy claimed that the dogs were always the aggressor when it came to being intimate...that when they approached him, sniffed his crotch or his ass, he knew they might be sexually interested in him. If the animal began to hump his leg, that was a clear sign that the animal was into him. With that information and without missing a beat, the cop announced that Randy was under arrest.

When searching the residence downstairs under the terms of the search warrant signed by a Superior Court judge, we found reams of pornography. There were videos, diskettes, notebooks, magazines, posters, piles of yellowing papers about the "sexual revolution," photos of naked men with other naked men, with naked women, and naked children with one another, in every combination, in every conceivable pose and position, with captions underneath describing what you were looking at. (If there is an accurate description or caption under the photo, in international courts it is argued that explicit pornography may be considered educational material.)

We found a few weapons: an inoperative handgun, a machete, an old rifle and a partially disassembled WWII machine gun...an old Tommy gun. To say that we had no idea what we would find in this search is the greatest understatement of my career.

Of all the material in the rooms downstairs, all the magazines, photos, dildos, paraphernalia and the books, even the wagon wheel chandelier over his bed with life-sized posters of pornographic images, I was thoroughly shaken by only one thing: a yellowing *San Francisco Chronicle* news clipping taped to the wall next to a bookcase. There, gawking at me under the bathroom mirror, was an old article about the connection of abuse toward animals with abuse toward women and children. I had been interviewed by the *San Francisco Chronicle* some years back about the correlation among psychopathic and serial killers in their proclivity for exploring animal abuse, torture and mutilation before moving on to human abuse, torture or murder. My name and title were underlined, along with a quote from me: "Often the animal abuser practices on animals, later to turn his attention toward children and women." This case was truly vice versa; here the perpetrator started with children, then turned toward animals.

The discovery of that news clipping on the mirror is one of my closest encounters with mystery. Synchronicity: play on words, synchro-mystery. A reminder of connection, of intelligence completely outside my understanding and physically manifest. This mystery is foundational in my decision to share this narrative, in this very personal way.

Sleepy Hollow

When living on the edge of surprise, inviting surprise even, welcoming change and whatever energy field presents, what is it to care about the domestication narrative of the humanoid? That is, has this Earth's essence and potentiality been strengthened overall by human development, or completely undermined and disturbed by the Anthropocene (human impact)?

Maybe the answer is somewhere in between. No matter what, the result of human habitation on the Earth has been profound. The land has been changed forever; it is very unlikely that the prior balance can be restored. One definition of *reactionary* is to think we can go back to when things were all right. Isn't whatever we create, intentionally or unintentionally, a new paradigm, a new balance? At the moment, we enter a period of hundreds if not thousands of competing interests, none of which is new in human history, but on this scale it is mind boggling. And the game is rigged.

We humanoids make many decisions that are forced on many of the ecologies, the micro and macro systems upon which all life and all beings are dependent and interdependent. We are just beginning to consider the perspectives and the agency of other living beings. Recently I read of a proposal for an underpass or possibly an overpass to aid the mountain lions who traverse Highway 17 at Glenwood cutoff, in the hilly area between Santa Cruz and San Jose. In addressing the issue of the animals' safety, we discuss a quick fix, a reformation of sorts. The discussion must go deeper than that and must be about a more complex transformation. How do we do this? How does one stay calm, modest and humble yet creative in this undertaking? How does one study, encourage and implement transformation?

We must use our imaginations and our intelligences to propose a more inclusive, life-affirming perspective that is thoughtful and sensitive to other life forms. Despite everything that tells us we are a relatively new species, we think we are extra special: the pinnacle of rationality and intelligence. Truly, we must step back from that flawed unique position to study, investigate, and delve into history, anthropology, biology, physics and botany for information about our place and how to proceed. History provides us with a great review of the results of our actions.

According to social psychologist Jonathon Haidt, those of conservative bent value loyalty, authority and sanctity. Liberal-leaning folks tend to value fairness, care and liberty. Libertarians are all about liberty. The science of the industrial age fomented new technology to make work more efficient, move us around the planet, let us communicate with one another at all times of day and night. We were born in an epoch which gives some of us free time to read, money to spend and choices to access the written word outside the libraries of the elite, outside the monastery walls of the holy fathers. These machines, *deus ex machina*, from printing presses to tablets and ebooks, became the moving force that delivered us to this place in the present and to our current dependence on fossil fuels. Man's contribution to creation is to replicate his god-self in this manner, his own image and likeness, to dominate and control the physical world based on technology and science. Woman's stereotypical role and contribution under patriarchy has been to carry, reproduce and be caregiver for more little humanoids, among other tasks.

Many of us believe everyone should have, at the minimum: water, nutritious food, some shelter, clothing to protect them from the weather. Recently, according to the United Nations, human rights include healthcare, education, and the opportunity for self-determination. It is argued that we ought to strive to provide our species these options out of justice, human-heartedness, compassion, even duty. It is the Golden Rule, to do unto others as you would have them do unto to you, a completely nonpartisan maxim, one that we can all embrace.

How do these perspectives hold up against the devastation wrought on the resources of this planet by providing for the basic needs of 7.2 billion (and growing) of us? The demands we make on the Earth are neither tenable nor sustainable. The number of daily births is double the number of deaths, and Earth's human population continues to grow beyond our ability to care for those human lives. What looks like indifference, selective compassion, or turning our faces away from others in need is based in bigotry, discrimination, racism and even fascism. We are overwhelmed, overloaded like the Earth, reeling under the weight of what is to be done. This *dis-ease*, this unease, this attempt at resolve may be a virulent combination of pathological altruism and compassion fatigue leading to burnout, anxiety and fear.

It is postulated that humanoids ought to dominate the Earth, that our perceptions of the scientific method, measurement and linearity ought to prevail upon all other ways of thinking and that through technology, we are moving toward a hegemony of humanism. The price tag includes the extinction of many species because of calamitous clear-cutting forests, drilling, fracking and mining. The price tag includes air pollution, water contamination, climate change and the myth that geoengineering (that is, science and technology) can save us. To address population concerns, the Chinese Communist Party tried to limit human reproduction and while somewhat successful for a time, the experiment flies against the ballast of human liberty.

As we sit reading or listening to this, we grapple with these problems because we are among the privileged. The technology we adore and despise has made this diatribe possible. Do we not care for our families, whether biological or chosen, more than we care for our neighbors? Do we care for those whose values we share, and not for those who are out of sight or with whom we vehemently disagree? And what about those other species—plants and animals, trees, rivers and mountains—that are ignored, disrupted, spoiled by our solipsistic thinking and selfish antics?

My version of Sleepy Hollow began the night of a major 6.9 earthquake in a quiet, touristy area of northern California known as Surf City, a few miles from the epicenter in mid-October, 1989. Since my move from Chicagoland five years earlier, I had been initiated into California's wide range of natural weather events, which were completely unfamiliar to my Midwestern upbringing. The urban/suburban experience of tornado, thunderstorm and blizzard seemed mild in comparison to the El Niño, La Niña, flooding, mudslides, droughts, wildfires, tsunami brand of California weather events. Top it off with a few temblors, some minor shaking and teaser earthquakes, and it all made for some good stories on visits back East.

When "The Big One" hit one late Tuesday afternoon in October 1989, I was at my job in the Santa Cruz SPCA, the county animal shelter, and profoundly unprepared for the experience. The ground shook, it rolled, and tumbled. The low bass rumble became vibrating waves ever louder, followed by a long, frightening, explosive train roaring underfoot whose engine seemed about to pierce the surface of the Earth. The walls leaned back and forth, shelves fell and cracked, windows broke and crashed on the concrete, the roadway and the horizon swayed drunkenly. These forty-five seconds seemed like forever. My nerves were sincerely jangled, I was wobbly, and well, I just pretended, like everyone else, that I was fine. At the time, I was in the uniform of an Animal Services Officer, my call name G-23, and I wore a California State Humane Officer badge. In times of stress, people look to those of us in uniform for answers to quell the storm, to assuage their fears.

Neighbors of the Live Oak animal shelter wandered dazed into the street. No one was hurt. We checked on staff and the animals. We walked the perimeter and the interior of the shelter wherein resided 125–150 various types of domestic animals, mostly dogs and cats, a couple of donkeys, some rabbits and a few guinea pigs. Everyone was okay. Power was out and we had a single landline phone that was working. We turned off the gas in case of leaks and started up the generator that would keep our portable radios charged, maintain radio communication with law enforcement, and keep the lights on. Immediately, our neighbor on the corner asked if we could run power to her saltwater aquarium to keep her fish alive. We moved her fish tank into the cat building kitchen and ran an extension cord to the pump. Luckily for the fish, the cats did not spend any time in the kitchen.

We made plans for who was staying at work and who was going home, and we waited with that single phone line, a few lights, and consistent reminders of what had transpired in the form of aftershocks. Sirens and dark and silence blanketed us that night. The energy was like nothing I had experienced until then, nor since. The animals were quiet. It seemed no one moved except to breathe, or on tiptoe. And we were, all of us, all species, wide awake.

After dark, radio communication alerted us to escaped horses from the west side of town. We had no sightings. A coworker and I traded off patrolling for the horses until we were directed to stay in the shelter, without a more specific location for the horses. Around 10 pm, a report came in that four to six horses had been spotted on 41st Avenue, a busy shopping area. The horses were headed toward the freeway.

I responded, in our radio-communications lexicon. I think about the word "respond" having the Latin root *respons*: pledge, promise. Root words for responsibility, despondent, spontaneity. Language rarely quite describes what the action is, nor the intensity, emotion, motivation or intention of such an action. There was a call and I responded in an animal shelter vehicle, a white Ford van with flashing yellow lights, Santa Cruz SPCA Animal Rescue and puppy paws painted in an optimistic bright blue on the sides and back of the van. I maintained radio contact with the shelter and County Communications on my patrol, first on the freeway and then along 41st Avenue, doubling back along the Highway 1 frontage road.

At night, in what had come to be my hometown, on that night of the earthquake with no power, no street lights, no gas stations, no store lights, no stoplights, no traffic, no signs of life at all—it was eerie. *Looking for horses, oh yeah.* I was startled by the voice over the radio: Horses seen on the freeway, Highway 1 near 41st Avenue.

I got back on Highway 1 at 7th Avenue, heading south toward 41st. All was quiet and still and very dark. I had my yellow flashing lights on, creeping down the right lane, squinting in the headlight-lit darkness. I had just passed the dimly lit 41st Avenue exit when suddenly, I mean like they dropped out of the sky, four horses running at full speed raced by the driver's side of my vehicle moving in the opposite direction, nostrils flaring, close enough to the van that I could have reached out the window and touched them. Two of them glared at me; I could see the whites of their determined, intense eyes as they raced past me, north into the dark. I fumbled with my radio, braked, pulled to the side of the freeway. I was trembling. I spoke into the transmitter and heard my raised voice say, "They are here."

Then I collected myself: "G-16, County Communications, G-23 reporting four horses running against traffic, fast lane on Highway 1 southbound at 41st, at full speed." While on the radio, I peered in my side-view mirror to try to see the horses. All I saw was a pair of headlights coming my direction. As soon as the fact of the headlights registered with me, those headlights disappeared, they were gone. Faster than a snap of the fingers.

"County Communications, G-23 reporting vehicle versus horses Highway 1 southbound between 41st and Bay/Porter."

Around 10 pm on the night of the earthquake, a young man of twenty-seven was driving his compact pickup to his home in Aptos after fixing a friend's hot water heater when he struck, or rather was struck by, two horses on Highway 1. A single passenger, he was traveling approximately 65 miles an hour with no time to react, to brake or skid. He never saw them coming. He was decapitated as the animals' bodies smashed through the front windshield. One horse was killed instantly and the other had to be euthanized at the scene of the accident.

Southbound Highway 1 was closed for eight hours as the authorities took measurements and photographs and removed wreckage. The mangled bodies of the two horses were moved by dump truck to the animal shelter, where they were wrapped in white sheets out of respect while awaiting pick-up by a rendering company thirty-six hours later. The two other horses escaped injury and were found later that night at the State Park Drive exit off of Highway 1, approximately six miles away from my sighting, and returned without further incident to the park rangers' stable. There were only four horses loose, not six as reported.

~

During the following week, we went on to remove animals from a downtown pet store and to evacuate little red-eared slider turtles and goldfish from the Woolworths on the Pacific Mall. We helped people reunite with their missing cats and runaway dogs, and the shelter boarded dogs and cats until folks could find alternative housing. Our census doubled to more than 300 animals of all types. We were plenty busy. For months.

I went to court, to counseling, found an animal communicator, and began collecting horse icons until there were too many to display in my 300-square-foot cabin. I had enough animals in front of me to look after at that time to spend too much time grieving the ones behind me. Optimistic then, I think of it now as resilience. And then I think of resolve.

~

Two thousand pounds of animal flesh crashes at significant opposing velocity into three thousand-plus pounds of machinery encapsulating a one-hundred-eighty-pound human male.

That day in October some thirty plus years ago, the first of many another day, I became witness to the grand clash of animal and machine, nature and humanoid, the real nightmare. The headless horseman's clattering hooves in the dark may visit my dreams every now and then, but what I remember is the wild, whale-eyed look in the eyes of those horses as they passed my driver's-side window that night. They reflect my own, very personal legend of sleepless hollow. What was in that glance toward me as those horses raced to their death? *It could be you*, is what I heard as the answer, and I have heard that refrain often these passing years. Now I know—not only that it might have been me who lost my human life that night but that it might have been me doing the running. California brought me here and California, in one way or another, will take me away.

Addendum

If you have never seen a horse drop, it is a truly jarring experience. This is 1,000 pounds of flesh that suddenly falls over like an avalanche. The ground shakes beneath you; there is a change in the air as the movement of that much dense matter through space is sudden and unexpected, an avalanche reduced to a snowball.

There we stand with the lame mare who is completely spent, on the hard, cold, rocky ground in the night, her hot breath slowing as her eyes roll back into their sockets. Scavengers, probably coyotes, grow impatient behind the chaparral. The usual way of the world is suspended, out of respect for what is transpiring. Still she is alive, but just barely.

We can intercede the way that some do, and sometimes we do, in these stories; or we can witness, or do more than witness by holding a candle along the way. Our knowledge and resolution are ineffective, our trusty problem-solving put aside for the stacking of the *now*, vertical time. We are caught, then enter willingly into frozen moments of receivership, that is, being fully present within the present.

In paradoxical relationship, in a dream state as well as a conscious one, we are listening. Hearkening. Vigilant. Listening with an intuitive consciousness that is as close to unconscious in subjective spontaneity as one can get. Like music, like the wilderness, like art. Our analytical knowledge is suspended to enter a direct path to realms beyond the spatial-temporal and attend to what Jung, and before him, Heraclitus, called *enantiodromia*. The yin/yang, fish-chasing-one-another's-tails moment running with the fully present as it changes polarity. While opening, listening and receiving, the observer is no longer separate from the observed, settling with an understanding beyond this realm yet completely within it. Rather than a division of otherness with the mare, we are the subject, within her consciousness, close up, participating in this inexplicable event...fused within the form of an Other, linked to openness and the transcendence of her life slipping away. A concrescence. This is the imaginal province made real.

We are drawn back to the mare by who knows what, like the way we lost time last night in the mystery of the vagus nerve's relaxation and dream world; maybe it was the coyotes' yellow eyes, the bone-chilling damp draft, the waning moon from behind cloud cover. But we are back, the mare is dead and now cold, and we notice with tears running down our faces that she is in peace. We place a warm hand on her chest, stroke her muzzle, wish her safe travels. We promise we will not forget.

Wider and Wilder than Wildlife

One day, the very excited woman's voice came over the amplified speakerphone to our animal shelter representative: "There is a monster in the garden shed!"

Calmly, the shelter worker asked, "What kind of monster?"

"You need to get over here right away!" When her panic caught up with the question, the woman said, "Oh, well, he's a *giant* rat…but he's old, very old and gray…with a long tail. He has beady eyes and sharp teeth. And, and," she said, voice rising in excitement, "he has…*human hands*."

The worker, very calmly: "Okay, that's an opossum, they live here in California and all over the United States. He won't hurt you. What's your address, so we can check him out and assure you he is all right?"

~~~

The shelter visitor at the counter held a covered cigar box tightly in her hand, carrying it like an offering.
~~~

She had been very patient, waiting in line in the animal shelter lobby for her turn. When she opened the box, there, standing alert on a long twig diagonal across the box, cushioned by leaves, was a monarch butterfly. The delicate ochre wings fluttered slightly. The bright orange-and-black segmented highlights and black-outlined white spots shone with marked intricacy and perfection. The black fuzzy butterfly body seemed sharply exaggerated next to the washed-out, whiskered face of an old Colonel Sanders-type guy in a brown suit and tie, chewing on the stub of a cigar on the inside cover of the box.

"Her wing," she said, "her wing is torn." Simply stated. Just a fact. Wing torn. Tissue-paper-thin wing. Peering into the box at the front counter, Tom looked at her and looked at the butterfly, a little smile forming in the corners of his mouth. "She can't fly," the woman said, seeking eye contact with Tom. "She has come such a long way…"

Tom, a seasoned shelter worker, thoughtful and sensitive, was dying of AIDs-related illnesses, a Kaposi sarcoma visible under his open-throated shirt. He looked back at her, hard-to-read Tom with that smile. "Don't know if we can help her. I know the veterinarian is too busy to see you. But I have an idea. How do you feel about trying something?" There was assent in the woman's eager nod.

Together now behind the counter, the two of them bent over the cigar box on a desk in the office. They worked with superglue to close the tear in the wing, using the point of a safety pin to smooth the glue, and held paper clips underneath the wing to hold it in place while the glue dried. Together they were sentinels there, to prevent other butterfly body parts from straying into the oozing wet glue. Talking in low voices, they congratulated each other on their steady hands, looking down at the shocked yet sedate butterfly. As the lid of the cigar box closed, the woman left the shelter with a little smile forming in the corners of her mouth.

We heard from her later that the procedure appeared to be a success. She reported that the butterfly was brushing softly against the lid of the cigar box by the time she returned home. An hour later she watched the monarch fly away. A gushing letter of appreciation for Tom went into his personnel file. The woman became a shelter volunteer, attended Tom's funeral, and forevermore was our go-to person for butterfly wing repairs.

On the scale of acceptable wildlife, wildlife that would be encouraged to coexist with humans, butterflies and songbirds are probably the top rated among city dwellers, while hawk, deer and coyote come next. There is a notable powerful super PAC of cats who thrive in the wild, with the help of an army of feral cat caretakers. Mourning doves, belonging to the same family (*Columbidae*) as pigeons, are admired by urbanites because of their sweet soulful call.

There is in-fighting among the "more acceptable animal" advocacy groups: the Audubon Society decries the impact of outdoor cats on the songbird population. Research is scanty, controversial and inconclusive. Marine mammal people say that the cat disease toxoplasmosis has crept into coastal waters, diminishing the otter population. Dog people say that coyotes are a threat to their small dogs. Cat people say that coyotes are predating not only household cats but also feral cats. Backyard birders say the raptors discourage songbirds from nesting. It is believed that pigeons carry disease (flying rats) despite their cousins, the domestically bred white doves, who are released at Stow Lake in Golden Gate Park to celebrate weddings, funerals and holidays. Chukars, a kind of partridge, also bred, said to represent love in Northern India and Pakistan, are often released in city parks following amorous rituals. Their survival rate in the wild is dismal.

Nuisance wildlife are called varmints but also vermin, some of whom coexist with us easily in the urban environment. They are, not in the order of popularity or population: raccoon, opossum, skunk, gopher, rat, mouse, pigeon. But no one says, "Eradicate them all!" the way they do for the less-fortunate muskrat, prairie dog, weasel, rabbit and coyote, among others, who are brutally hunted as "pests" in other parts of California. I understand that in some areas of this country, at least a few of these animals are hunted for food, some for their fur and sometimes just for fun.

Raccoon coats and caps, rabbit and possum meat, pigeon shoots and coyote contests abound outside our urban centers.

Amid the urban bird order, there are hierarchies of desirability as well. We humans are kind of fickle. Corvids (crows, ravens, jays) and raptors (hawks, falcons, owls) are on the outs, on the reasoning that they go after songbird nests and eggs. Interestingly, without predators such as hawks to keep them in check, the corvids, opportunistic feeders that they are, will decimate a songbird population. Beneficent owls are known to hunt gophers, another pest for whom there is little tolerance, although owls in the city are few.

While protecting their young in spring, starlings and blackbirds are loud, bossy, and dive-bomb our heads as we go into the grocery store; plus, they are not indigenous. In a kind of funny anti-immigration policy among species, there is more cachet to being characterized as "native wildlife." However, what is native is relative. Most of us came here as immigrants, to the detriment of the indigenous First Nations. Animal species migrate too.

No one seems to mind that non-native cats, dogs and coyotes tangle with raccoons, opossums, rats, mice, and pigeons; that is just the natural order of things. Except when there is a chance of rabies contamination. At this juncture, we introduce the most unpopular of unpopular wildlife: bats. Batty. Blind as a bat. Okay as a superhero but no good as a coexisting species, they are thought to be creepy, and can carry viral disease. They get in our hair. They have horns and devil eyes. We have some idea about their benefits to our ecology. We know that they thrive on another of our varmints, biting insects, particularly mosquitos. Still we can't find the beneficent in them except as Halloween stencils in the window.

The animal that is the insect—now that is one big, complicated story. Insects are the most diverse class of invertebrates, with more than a million different species. Which ones do we like? Which ones can we live with? Does a fruit fly have a right to life? What about a mite? And then we think about all that is unknown about the sea, expanding the invertebrate class to ocean and sea inhabitants like coral and alga and yet-to-be identified species.

Avoiding examination by the urbanite is the wild snake, garter or garden or king or gopher. Snakes live in the interstices, the in-between places, beneath and behind, out of sight. So far, few urban hominids aim to kill or protect or even acknowledge their existence. The city might just be the safest place on the planet to be a snake.

Pigeon Problems

Want to notify yours, the owner with some who is working he hire and some tenants, in combination, they treat very bad the pigeons. The tenants feel afraid to him. The pigeon comes and back only to eat. The pigeon don't live and stay lasting. The guy that they work for them, they kill 2 pigeons today and before 3 dead for them. The pigeon only eat and go. They are innocent people not like dog and cat. They living and words is very different. To killing only for coming to eat, not right. I want to notify you and note to our President Obama. This my copy of testimony to them.

I want you call the owner, Tool Brake and Wheel Service Center, 3500 24th Street, Sam Hoyer. Tell him stop those guys, stop order. Some tenants feel afraid to him for the rent increase. Stop, please. He don't like me because I live 41 years in my apartment and he want me to move for the pigeon come and back to me. He try to make me sick. I am 72 years old, alone and the phone of me is sometimes not working. He don't like me too because I am from Cuba of Fidel Castro and

Che Guevara. I was secretary of them and I am communist. I came to here make my mother happy to stay with my brother, who against Castro now. All when comes to USA, left my ideology communist. Now come here and work with crazy people and thugs.

Living in here and don't like me that they rather me to die or get sick. They aggravate to treat them and kill pigeon front of me to make me sick and suffers. They do on purpose innocent animal but God is upstairs they will be punish. I suffer too much: lost my mother, father and husband, since USA. I work to translate 37 years until retire from Army of Presidio secretary of Colonel Thrache until Presidio close. Husband die. 72 years old, alone, only I have pigeon. I come back to Cuba when Obama will stop the embargo of Cuba but I feel really sad to leave my innocent pigeons.

Pigeon was the first animal on the world, very innocent. The picture of God I have a pigeon above on bed. Fidel, too, is animal for the communist is pigeon landing on shoulder during revolution, that Cuban people know God like them, like pigeon and like me.

Please stop order. I clean yard but not complain. They don't allow me to clear caught ones. The worker of him put something block the way for me. No more. I can't go clean yard every day. I did not want to have excuse to show how pigeon dirty the yard. I want justice and stop them to aggravate them and treat them very bad. They put snake close to the pigeon and my window. Unfortune thing, the pigeons don't eat today.

The communist people are right, they don't feel

afraid. They treat me like the guy that he work with husband hit the wife but I teach them with my husband not hit the wife. The wife not afraid.

Some tenants, they want to get my apartment 5 and they try to provocate me and scare me and kill pigeon. Put maya [wire] *on the roof, kill pigeon, innocent and against the law. Animals only comes and back for eat. The owner Sam Hoyer in combination with some Cubans don't like me because I like Obama and Fidel Castro. They put wood on the yard for me and for the pigeon don't eat and I clean the yard, I tell them. Make me sick to move the house 41 years in here and they send people behind when I go to the store, they try to kill me, with a dog, a bicycle and other thing. They call the policeman take a picture of me and the pigeon. When I pass the street, they try to hit me with the car on 23rd and Mission Street from the BART station. They don't like me because I was support of Fidel Castro and the Che Guevara.*

I came to here to make my mother happy for my brother. But I was interview for FBI and when he said to me Oct 13, 1966, I will just get to USA. I said I am never a communist of Che Guevara. Lie. But not afraid now. I need protection for me and my pigeon inside home and yard for pigeon and outside too. They want my home is against the law. What they doing look like Mafia but in my sad war I will not let guy, very dangerous even, abuse and action to hurt animal.

With this, talk to the people and make owner comes to my home. See what they do it. Please help me.

Terrible hard. Thanks, waiting yours to take care it. Very aggravation.

May God and pigeon bless you and your family,

Josefina Garcia
S. Van Ness, San Francisco

Rat-a-Tat-Tat

The report was disturbing; the complaint seemed unlikely, it couldn't be accurate.

We discussed it on Friday afternoon and the plan was to meet at the residence the next morning. I spoke to the landlord, who was cordial and conciliatory while young children cried in the background. I reached him on his mobile phone after 6 pm that Friday night. His amiability challenged an initial assumption that he was a slumlord. We couldn't check because it was Friday afternoon. The Health Department, Environmental Health, Code Enforcement, the City attorney, and Risk Management of San Francisco were not answering the phone. Bureaucracy was turned off, shut down for the weekend. The watch commander at the police department said he was unable to respond or commit to back up; he understood the public safety risk but it was impossible for him to deploy units for such an unknown situation. We could call them when we knew more.

The next morning, we collected gloves, masks, Tyvek suits, wore our heavy boots and long-sleeved shirts, and drove to a South of Market transitional neighborhood. This area was slowly being gobbled up by speculative real estate development and becoming increasingly gentrified since the Westfield shopping mall had opened a few years back. This transition had been incomplete because the single resident occupancy (SRO) hotel was home not only to ten single men but also to seven extended families, including twelve children and four senior adults over sixty-five. There were at least eight ethnicities represented: Nicaraguan, Mexican, Filipino, Somali, Vietnamese, Korean, Irish, East Indian.

Next door to the building in question was a different story: the tinted windows of huge tour buses stopped at the renovated and gated Hotel Morgana. Visitors from Japan, France, Brazil and England disembarked, twenty-five or thirty at a time, filling the hotel to capacity, tourists who hardly flinched at the small 10x10-foot accommodations with a shared water closet and kitchen and separate bathing rooms in the hallway on three floors. Of the owners, one entrepreneur paid the hotel tax and the other real estate speculator paid the real estate tax, both contributions doing their part to keep the wheels of the bureaucracy greased from 9 to 5, Monday through Friday…well, maybe only until 3 pm on Friday. Because as we know, the mayor, the supervisors and their aides had left the building, and so had the rest of *governmentium.*

So here they sat, side by side, two hotels with identical floorplans: one an aged, dilapidated, rundown SRO whose clients were referred by judges, homeless advocates, mental health clinics and the Red Cross; the other, a middle-income tourist hotel that catered to international visitors from developing countries on various continents.

The contact zone for this event was created by one Jack McArdle.

We met on the stoop leading up to the SRO: Jack, Ahmeet (the landlord), Andrea (hipster advocate from nonprofit Pets Are Wonderful Support, PAWS), a uniformed animal cop named Aramis, and me. All of us but Jack had discussed the plan the night before. Jack's social worker from the Homeless Advocacy Group, Heather, was in the middle of an online test and couldn't be interrupted this morning; apparently Social Services didn't work on the weekends either. Jack agreed to allow us to inspect his room, where he allegedly harbored a colony of what Jack described euphemistically as his pet rats.

Jack was a veteran of the Gulf War, George H.W.'s, George-the-First War, the First War Against Saddam Hussein, one of many for oil, whose win resulted in the earth-scarring oil fires in Kuwait. It was Jack's first war too, in the air force as a mechanic. When Jack came back from the Gulf he was sick, he says, with Gulf War Syndrome. Jack became frustrated and angry when he couldn't hold down a job. He liked his booze and his weed and later, because it was cheaper though more addictive, crystal methamphetamine, which was his undoing.

Jackson Kent McArdle had been incarcerated on drug charges and sentenced to a four-year sentence in the California Substance Abuse Treatment Facility and State Prison in Corcoran, California. In the tortuous tedium of his incarceration, he had learned to socialize the wild rats with whom he shared his cell.

Jack brought this skill to his second-floor room in the SRO next to the Hotel Morgana in the South of Market area, close to downtown San Francisco, in the early years of the new millennium. Jack's room was hardly bigger than a prison cell but for three narrow and lengthy windows always open, facing the street. Because the buzzer in his room didn't work, a butler's bell on a long string hung out the window closest to the steps of the porch on the street, for use by friends and foes alike to alert Jack of their presence. Our entourage consisted of both.

Entering his room, the scent was a combination of decomposing flesh, ammonia, rotting food, fecal matter, sweat and dirty socks. We were all grateful for the generosity of those windows. The smell was thickest close to the floor, where it seemed that a permeable wall of dense, gaseous humidity clung to the air. Difficult as it is to imagine, a mere doorknob and a solid wooden door kept this disturbing level of chaos behind it.

The putrid stench sent a rush of adrenaline through my body as I began to search visual cues in the room.

I noticed slight movement throughout the room as Jack's rats peeked out from under the blanket on the bed, behind the bedpost, in the couch cushions, or suddenly scurried across the room's obstacle course, a mountain of clothing, furniture, newspaper, electronics and food containers. Other little groups of rats seemed to inhabit other visible open space in and around the dresser and under the twin bed/futon couch. There was a shoebox-sized Tupperware container that held 40 or so baby rats, "pinkies" they are called when sold at pet stores as food for snakes or to labs for experimental use. And of course, Jack's tiny, dark closet was the major nesting area, covered with scraps of shredded cotton stuffing, material and paper. A framed pastoral landscape print covered holes in the drywall the size of golf balls. All around the molding, the floorboards, and along the floor, the rats had gnawed holes, drilling access into the walls.

Here's the story: Jack had at least 232 brown rats, *Rattus norvegicus* (not including the pinkies) in his room. Jack was a hoarder. Jack and his rat pack were holding hostage all the immigrants with uncertain legal status at 309 RueLa in this SRO South of Market, residents who had come to expect rats flying out of those windows at the front entry, who expected to chase rats out of the shower, from the kitchen and back down the hallway toward Jack's room. But when next door residents/clients at 311 RueLa, the Hotel Morgana, began to complain about rat sightings in the hallway, rats jumping out of dresser drawers and scratching behind the walls at night, the management of the Morgana made a complaint to Animal Services. We do not respond to rodent infestations, we said. This is different, they said.

The damage was done. Jack was probably in his late forties, tall and lanky, dressed in blue jeans and a t-shirt, high-top Nikes and an United States Air Force bomber jacket. He had a swarthy, freckly complexion, sunken blue eyes and no front teeth, and his thin lips pursed often to maintain control of the resultant saliva as he spoke. His coarse rust-colored hair stuck out from a black watch cap pulled tightly over his ears and forehead. Tiny holes, little tears and rips in his jeans and shirt—I was suddenly feeling claustrophobic—the material had nappy little protrusions; his shoes, the same thing, rough-chewed through rubber and plastic; and finally I noticed the little cuts and scratches on his face and neck. I searched for other exposed flesh and his hands confirmed my fear that he was also the target of the rats' mercenary appetites.

Because Jack may have been exposed to typhus, hantavirus, or worse case, bubonic plague, he was quarantined for his safety and for public safety. But not until Monday, when those who governed returned to their offices. Then the phone rang off the hook from Environmental Protection, the Health Department, Risk Management, et al. Even the mayor's office called; this could be an international incident. The Hotel Morgana owners, entrepreneurs and investors wanted an immediate explanation.

There is a theory of philosophy that rats and roaches are metaphoric rhizomes, and that as we destroy the ecology of the planet, rats and roaches and probably other creatures deep in the ocean we have yet to identify will find the hibernation and incubation places that promise their survival—and later, when conditions are right, will burst forward in proliferation of life.

And sometimes, life is just that, survival with whatever is in front of you.

~~~

Culture is not linear nor hierarchical. Culture in this context means our rights and our rites, our social behavior and values, our beliefs. Reaching for the pinnacle of human reason or causality, even if we believe it is the ultimate truth, will not suffice. Belief will not make it so.

In philosophy, *teleology* is a belief that progress is the ultimate purpose of nature. Progress dwells at the tip-top of the most advanced theories of mathematics, science and technology, all endeavors of the human mind. On the other hand, the *rhizomatic* model of knowledge and culture includes the agents of a holistic ecology: earthly, heavenly, gravitational, atmospheric. All of that is *other*, outside the human mind. Systems are interdependent, even though at a great distance from one another, visible and invisible, sometimes asymmetrical, unmeasurable, and appearing in dysphoric ways.
~~~

Add the internet, big government and global corporations, war and migration, now climate change, we survive in a chaos of complex, dense forces bumping up against one another. The rhizome is always becoming: Never the same from one minute to the next, always moving toward something other than what it is, resilient, adapting, looking for balance.

Rhizomatic culture is not lurching toward any function, purpose or progress. Rather, it is in the middle of the ordered chaos that is being and becoming where it is exposed, most visible and most vulnerable. This is where new stories, new narratives will imagine a new culture, and extend into the rhizome horizontally.

Nietzsche said that there is a qualitative difference between culture and civilization. Culture takes civilization, chews it up and spits it out. Taoist culture is water wisdom, filling all the low-lying spots in our landscape, collecting in puddles, traveling in large and small groups of wanderers, rats, roaches, bedbugs…small tribes of survivors, visionaries and outsiders…harmonizing by just getting by. The meek will inherit the Earth.

Passion and Appetite

The ancient Zapotec nation of central Oaxaca took the puma, the ocelot and the jaguar very seriously. Sighting one of these wild cats was considered a gift from the Great Spirit.

The Zapotec believed that extraordinary women and men were called at an early age by ancestors and by their looks to flatten their heads, extend their lips, file their teeth into sharpened incisors, and tattoo stripes upon their bodies. It was thought that these shamans straddled both worlds; shape-shifting, they embodied the jaguar. Coexisting with jaguar and living within this magic would bring fertility, good health, adequate crops, fruitful gathering and prosperous hunting to the community, their families and groups. They organized their villages and communities around the principles of large wild cat worship. One such ritual involved anthropophagy—eating human flesh—during which a shaman elder woman consumed, that is, ate young Zapotec boys to express the jaguar's appetite. Being chosen for this sacrifice was considered an honor.

While in Oaxaca City, amid learning about the Zapotec culture and habits, a tiger visited me in a dream. She was a standard orange-and-black-striped Bengal tiger. Privileged, I inhabited the body of this great tiger in my dream. I looked through her eyes, walking stealthily, gracefully, strong and steady. Walking in the body of the tiger, I came upon open, arid land with pointed agave cactus where I hunted lizards and small mammals, surrounded by layers of mountains, some gray and rocky, others green and hilly. I felt an immense power within me that startled me awake to loud drumming and whistling on the street near our courtyard residence. This was the beginning of Dia de los Muertos, the Day of the Dead celebration in Oaxaca. Immediately, I knew I was meant to write about Tatiana.

~

On Christmas Day in 2007, the appetites and passions of three young men from San Jose, out on a caper on the holiday, bored and aloof probably, smoking and drinking together, found themselves in a face-to-face encounter with a 250-pound Siberian Amur tiger (*Panthera tigris tigris*) named Tatiana at the San Francisco Zoo. By the end of their antagonism, although they denied any interaction, one teenage man, seventeen-year-old Caleb Salazar, Jr. and Tatiana, the four-year-old Siberian tiger, had been killed. The other two young men involved were brothers,

Adnan and Kalid Singh, nineteen and twenty-three respectively. They were rushed to the hospital. In the hours following the incident, Investigator Vicky Martin of the San Francisco Police Department interviewed the Singh brothers at SF General Hospital, where their injuries were photographed and the men were treated for significant bites and scratches to their heads and arms. There was no provocation, they claimed. They had only been eating nachos. The tiger must have been hungry.

Tatiana's body was *evidence* in a wrongful death rather than the *victim* of a wrongful death. Due to the uproar (pun intended) and because the chain of evidence needed to be preserved, even on Christmas night, I drove two hours from a holiday cut short in Santa Cruz to the San Francisco shelter to meet with the investigating officers and the director of the shelter. As "homicide" was involved, the SFPD took over the case. The impact of the killings reverberated throughout the human world as well as the animal welfare community. No charges were filed nor arrests made. Lawsuits followed for the humans. Years of review of the safety and wellbeing of the animals at the San Francisco Zoo followed this tragedy.

Many have said that Tatiana's escape jump was an anomaly. Her feat in traversing a 29-foot moat to jump a 12-foot 9-inch wall was extremely unlikely. Despite the denials of the young men, experts hypothesized that Tatiana was agitated and motivated to attack by an angry prey drive induced by the erratic poking and provoking actions of the young men taunting her proximate to her concrete containment.

For Marlina Salazar, Caleb Salazar's mother, I am sure that Christmas Day has a different resonance since 2007. For me, the holiday has changed as well. In the years since Caleb's and Tatiana's deaths, the dominant public meaning of that day has been replaced by a private acknowledgement of the plight of captive animals and how much needs to be done. Tatiana's photograph still greets the public at the front door of the SF Zoo to this day and there is a mosaic sculpture of her on Telegraph Hill. Tatiana has been replaced by Martha, a sixteen-year-old Siberian tiger from Nebraska, now comfortably living in the glass-enclosed, reinforced tiger grotto, encircled by a raised and electrified fence.

In separate incidents, two United Kingdom zookeepers, both women, were killed by tigers, one in 2013 and the other in May of 2017. Cicip, a Malayan tiger and Padang, a Sumatran tiger were spared by the authorities. It was claimed that the captive-bred tigers, in each case, were doing what was natural to them. (The only and truly unnatural act is the way in which they were housed.)

According to the World Wildlife Fund, in 2015 there were more captive tigers in the U.S. than wild tigers in the world. Of the estimated 5,000 captive tigers (and the count may be as many as 10,000) here in the United States, only 350 are permitted and/or registered with the Zoological Association of America. More than 3,000 tigers living in Texas are privately owned. There are an estimated 3,900 tigers in the wild on the whole rest of the planet Earth.

Tiger Haven in Tennessee houses more than 250 various types of large cats in a 75-acre sanctuary. Many have been "donated" from circuses and roadside shows.

Four white tigers more than twelve years old are kept in a glassed-in aquarium in downtown Houston without access to outdoors or direct sunlight. In Denver, three more tigers owned by the same company are also kept in an aquarium display.

There is a Siberian mix tiger named Tony who lives at a truck stop in Louisiana.

Big Cat Rescue in Tampa, Florida is home to more than 100 large feline exotics.

A Las Vegas magic act became a spectacle displaying the beauty and grace of white Bengal tigers under the discipline of Siegfried Fischbacher and Roy Horn, Las Vegas entertainers. At a 2003 Las Vegas Hotel Mirage performance, Mantacore, the albino Bengal tiger, jumped up and grabbed Roy by the neck, brought him down and dragged him across the stage in front of a stunned audience. After a ten-year recovery from his critical wounds, a partially paralyzed Roy and his partner Siegfried returned to the stage with Mantacore at a fancy hotel on the Las Vegas strip, in a final act before both Mantacore and Roy retired. Until a few years ago, Siegfried and Roy continued to breed albino lions and tigers to make a very substantial living. Their net worth was north of $120 million in 2018.

Albino tigers do not exist in the wild; the albinos are mated with other albinos because they are "albino" unusual. The genetics of these bred animals result in many individuals with cleft jaws, crossed eyes or spinal abnormalities, as well as other birth defects that result in distortions of life and limb. These abnormal breeding lines must be neutralized.

Tiger farms in China raise the more common Siberian tigers specifically for their body parts; their tails, teeth and internal organs are considered an aphrodisiac in China as well as other countries including Thailand, the Philippines, United Arab Emirates and the United States. Albino lions are also raised in specialty breeding programs where brother and sister are mated for generations, aiming for the anomaly of color tone or lack thereof.

You may recall the 2011 release of fifty exotic wild animals in Zanesville, Ohio, followed by the suicide of owner Terry Thompson. It was reported that 61-year-old Thompson was a depressed Vietnam war veteran who collected wild animals for notoriety and fun. Of the 56 animals Thompson kept on his 73 acres, 49 were killed by police on October 18 and 19 in this rural area outside of Columbus, Ohio. The eight-hour hunt took down seventeen lions, eighteen tigers (*panthera tigris tigris*), three mountain lions, six black bears, one grizzly, a baboon and a wolf. From all statements, the animals were living in substandard and filthy conditions, fed by donations from neighbors and expired grocery store food.

The local sheriff, responding to complaints of neglect and cruelty, had visited the animal compound more than thirty times during that year. Everyone in the area knew about Terry Thompson's animals, including the veterinarians at the Columbus Zoo. The docile animals could be rented for the county fair, birthday parties or anniversaries. Staff from the zoo in Columbus and the USDA afterward commented that there were no other options but to massacre the animals to protect public safety.

⁂

At least seven states have passed laws that makes it illegal for whistleblowers to use recording equipment to document work done in the factory farming business. The so-called "Ag-gag" laws disallow anyone to bring an audio or video device into an agricultural operation with the intention of making conditions within the farm public. Interestingly, roadside zoos and exotic animal sanctuaries are considered agricultural operations, although this has been challenged in court. The Ninth Circuit Court of Appeals recently struck down a Utah Ag-gag law, ruling that it was overbroad. Nonetheless, Ag-gag laws are pending in North Carolina and Iowa.

These laws are designed to prevent investigative journalists and animal activists from undercover activities, squashing their attempts to expose the abuse, neglect and inhumane treatment at farms and in labs as well as in private collections, sanctuaries, and roadside zoos. All of these so-called animal enterprises are protected by the United States Animal Enterprise Terrorism Act of 2006.

Michael Jackson's animal menagerie included reptiles, snakes, giraffes, and an elephant given to him by Elizabeth Taylor. When Jackson was charged with child sexual abuse in 2005, he abandoned the famed Neverland property and many of the animals who lived there. His staff was to disperse the animals in the best possible ways by placing them with new owners. Both Michael Jackson's tigers and the Ringling Bros. Circus's fifteen cats went to Tippi Hedren's Shambala and to the American Sanctuary Association-certified Tiger Haven in Tennessee. The ASA president is Ms. Hedren, whom you may recall played the female lead in Alfred Hitchcock's 1963 film *The Birds*. Like Bob Barker, Doris Day and other celebrities, notoriety can give Hollywood notables credentials in the field of animal welfare.

~

In September 2017, Feld Entertainment, a transporter of tigers belonging to Ringling Bros. Circus, was moving fourteen tigers from Florida to Tennessee when a six-year-old female Bengal tiger named Suzy escaped from a truck into the night. Ultimately Suzy was hunted down by police in a predawn high-speed chase on a highway near Atlanta.

When Tiger Safari was hit by a tornado in May of 2015 in Tuttle, Oklahoma, no one was sure how many animals were housed there. It was believed that there were kangaroos, tigers, otters, lemurs, bears and leopards, as well as a number of birds and snakes. Within twenty-four hours, the police declared all were accounted for, despite the fact that no records were kept.

A fire broke out at the Greater Wynnewood Interactive Exotic Animal Park (also in Oklahoma) in March 2015, in which seven alligators and one crocodile died of toxic smoke inhalation. Seven of the eight animals were previously owned by Michael Jackson. It was believed the fire was intentionally set.

Apparently in Oklahoma, anything goes. On an eight-mile drive through the Arbuckle Wilderness Park near Ardale, Oklahoma, you can see and feed ligers, offspring of a male lion mating with female tiger; tigons, offspring of a male tiger mating with a female lion; liligers, offspring of a male lion mating with a female liger; and titigons, offspring of a male tiger mating with a female tigon. You get the picture.

Of the more than 2,400 zoos (also known as animal exhibitors) permitted by the United States Department of Agriculture, 350 are members of the AZA (Association of Zoos and Aquariums), which is not a regulatory body but has declared standards and proclaimed scientific reasons for existence. This is also true for the ZAA (Zoological Association of America). In the United States in 2017, there were 500 zoological facilities (including aquariums) supposedly existing for the conservation, captive breeding and research of exotic and threatened animals. Public education and recreation are a byproduct of zoos.

Thousands of various roadside zoos, sanctuaries and collectors have no such mandate or regulating body. The only laws overseeing these varied warm-blooded, regulated animals (*un*regulated animals include farm animals, those used for food and agriculture, and birds or reptiles) fall under the woefully inadequate 1966 United States Animal Welfare Act (AWA). This law is enforced by the United States Department of Agriculture Animal and Plant Health Inspection Service (USDA APHIS), a unit notably understaffed and unmotivated. The AWA was meant to uphold rigid standards in managing and inspecting facilities that house wild and dangerous animals throughout the country, as well as to regulate breeding, stocking and transporting animals, domestic, exotic and wild.

Even in the progressive Bay Area, the San Francisco Zoological Gardens and the East Bay Zoological Society in Oakland are only annually inspected. In the case of the East Bay Zoo, problems with fencing and peeling paint have persisted for years. Notably, as of mid-2018 there had been no updates on the USDA Inspections website since the Republican administration took office in 2016. When encouraged to allow third-party inspectors to assist, which would have included certification inspectors and state animal welfare stakeholders, the USDA declined that relief in May 2018. This does not bode well for animals.

Roadside zoos, animal exhibits, rescues and sanctuaries are often private enterprises and nonprofit organizations that, as stated above, have no standards whatsoever as to the care of their residents. These are so-called wild animals, also called exotic but also simultaneously considered domestic (or domesticized), who are held captive for display, human interaction and entertainment or for private enjoyment. *Domestic wild animals* is like saying "a black/white color."

Under the mantle of scholarly inquiry during the '60s and '70s, research studies forced interactions of nonhuman primates into families with humans to "domesticize" them, resulting in unethical and cruel practices. (See the film *Project Nim*.) As the animal grows into sexual maturity and becomes less controllable, he or she loses his/her value and begins to wreak havoc within the captive environment. Too often the results are incarceration in necessarily ironclad containment where, even in the best of circumstances, the animal suffers and caregiver safety becomes more challenging. This broad generalization has wide application for many captive animals, from turkeys to otters to primates. The continuation of this chaotic misnomer, the *domestic wild animal*, often captive-bred and removed from their mothers right after birth to be raised by human hand for commercial value, is inhumane and unethical.

Tigers and other powerful cats proliferate in this world of exotics. For whatever reason, big cats seem to have taken hold in our collective imagination: Cars, shoes and professional sports teams are named after them. However, the exploitative way we treat tigers is the way we treat most other exotic animals within a whole web of domination, neglect and misunderstanding. Whatever happened to stewardship?

Initially, I thought setting the animals free was the answer. Then I realized that in some ways, it is the principles of anarchy and libertarianism, the call of rugged individualism, no rules, that brought us here in the first place. In the U.S., anyone over the age of eighteen can own exotic and wild animals nearly anywhere in certain states, notably Alabama, Texas and Florida. In states like Alaska, it is unclear what is going on in unregulated and remote sections. After all, the United States *is* the "Lord of the Flies," oops, I meant "Land of the Free."

As an animal activist, my belief is that animals have moral agency; they have a right to live in accordance with their authentic natures, in a complex, healthy environment with the freedom to thrive. It might just be that the human appetite for "freedom" has placed nonhuman animals as a stand-in for our passion to be in the company of wildness. A reminder of our power over, we display a passionate version of a perverted wildness.

Our appetite grows to contain more and more, to control more and more. Colonization. Greed. Hubris. Arrogance. We think we know better, that we are smarter. *Together, if you do what I say, we will flourish. I will help you to bloom, to sow more seeds, to grow well.* I assure myself of my pure intention, my altruism (not unlike patriarchy), convinced that *you can trust that I will care for you better than you could possibly care for yourself. Sometimes, even against your will, I know what is good for you. You will thank me later. Only I can love you and treat you right. Only I can save you.*

A cult. A conversion. A con game. True freedom, interdependence and resultant wisdom are impossible while we dissemble in discord. We are in the throes of our passion for freedom, and of our appetite to control and maintain symbols of the wildness and freedom we have lost. Let us realize that this distortion is no longer acceptable. It no longer serves us; in fact, it will destroy us, as well as many of our animal relatives.

Death at the Door

New, the millennium wasn't supposed to scare us, but it did. We all worried that our dependence on technology would prove unreliable, traffic lights were expected to malfunction, we wouldn't be able to get fuel out of the gas pumps; trains and airplanes would go berserk because computers were not programmed beyond 1999. All the schedules and timekeeping capabilities in our modern computerized culture were predicted to go haywire. We stocked up on extra water, filled the gas tank, bought extra batteries, took out the camp stove, checked the pantry for canned food, made sure there was kerosene in case we had to hunker down. We had the whole weekend to prepare because New Year's Day 2000 was a Saturday.

That Monday, all fretting came to an end during the beginning of the new millennium because—you know what?—there was nary a hitch in our forward motion in time, a premonition of the twenty-first century hurtling forward.

Haywire is baling wire for hay. Sometimes farmers resort to using that baling wire to repair the tractor or the plow; eventually, things would break beyond the capacity of that hay wire to hold things together. Another thought behind the origin of haywire is when the baling machine that separates and ties each hay bale as it moves along the conveyor belt, the baler engine misfires, and all the baling wire gets tangled up in an ugly mess which takes weeks to unravel. I am sure there are other ideas about hay wire, each dependent on an active imagination. Fear of techno-haywire (my term) was prevalent at the end of the twentieth century. But on January 3, 2000, we returned to our sane and sound environments with a collective sigh of relief. We all went on with our so-called lives thinking we were on solid ground; we didn't need the haywire after all. This was the beginning of the millennium, the year of the 2000 campaign for the next president of the United States. Maybe things would go a little haywire.

Among the many species of dogs, from little one- to two-pound Chihuahuas to huge Great Danes and St. Bernard dogs weighing upwards of 200 pounds, there are dogs of various sizes who have been bred for their high-strung temperaments. Border collies, spaniels and terriers are intense dogs, generally. Fighting is in the bloodlines and history of dogs like Akita, Shar-Pei, Leonberger, Cane Corso, and Perro de Presa

Canario, among others. It is not nearly as exciting to fight little- or even medium-sized dogs.

A whole range of large-breed dogs with massive heads, jaws the size of a bear, and a penchant for aggression and protection are bred for their predatory, fighting or gamey dispositions. They are utilized for tracking boar and bear, for working cattle herds, for pulling down bulls by their lips and ears, for hunting, for fighting. They are named for lions and geographical places, or their chosen names are archetypical, named after mythical gods and goddesses, gangsters, despots, murderers, sociopaths. And many breeders of these dogs will tell you that these fighting traits have been bred in or out of them over generations.

That is why some well-socialized friendly dogs turn dangerous, and why some "dangerous dogs" of "dangerous breeds" (scare quotes all over this) turn friendly.

During the year following our delivery from our millennial techno-devolution, one week post-inauguration of George W. Bush's contested election, late one Friday afternoon on January, 26, 2001, Julie Welker (name changed), a thirty-three-year-old popular women's soccer coach at a local private college, returned to her San Francisco apartment in the upscale neighborhood of Pacific Heights. She carried a bag of groceries, intending to make tacos for dinner.

In the hallway approaching her apartment door, on the sixth floor at the end of the hallway, Julie was brutally attacked for six long minutes by two 125- to 140-pound adult Perro de Presa Canario dogs, an intact male named Hex and a fertile female named Juno, owned by two attorneys who lived down the hall in a neighboring unit. Julie, an accomplished athlete, had completed a marathon the week before this stunningly brutal event. She was bit seventy-seven times on all parts of her body by the out-of-control dogs and sustained mortal wounds to her neck and larynx. About one-third of her blood supply soaked into the maroon patterned carpet that night in front of apartment 600.

Stripped of her clothing by the dogs, lying naked in front of her partly opened door with the keys in the lock, weeping blood, Julie was still alive when paramedics arrived within ten minutes of the calls from frantic neighbors who thought a woman was being raped in the hallway. She died three hours later in San Francisco General Hospital while in emergency surgery.

The dogs were locked in the bathroom of apartment 604 down the hall when the San Francisco Police Department called Animal Services. It took three sedative darts, four men and two women, and more than two hours to remove the dogs from that room, put them on catch poles, load them into cages within a shelter vehicle, and deliver them to the animal shelter twenty minutes away, in the Mission District.

I think of myself as mild-mannered, brought up a good Catholic girl by middle class standards, with hardworking, staunch Midwestern values: polite, most would agree, and more than a little quirky. The kid on the block who administered the funerals for fallen chipmunks, roadkill squirrels and cat-caught birds, that was me. How else to explain my career with animals in animal shelters, undertaking animal welfare and protection?

The evening of that dog mauling, rather than animal advocate, I was acting in a public safety capacity to protect the human beings who lived in San Francisco—and who worked and volunteered in the shelter environment—from further contact with these dangerous dogs whose behavior and predatory aggression had just brought down a youthful, vibrant woman in the most unexpected and violent manner. If ever there were dangerous dogs, these were dangerous dogs.

Within thirty minutes of the dogs' arrival at the shelter, we had statements from the licensed co-owner of Juno and Hex, Michelle Bowler, who had been on the scene of the "accident." Hex was the attacking dog. Juno, the female, Michelle claimed was not involved. The other co-owner, Thomas Boyd, with Bowler's agreement, gave permission for Hex's immediate euthanasia. The next step was to get permission from the watch commander at SFPD to put Hex down, and that was accomplished. Hex was sedated and humanely euthanized with an overdose of a barbiturate by 8 pm that night.

Dogs are a bridge species, providing an insight and conveyance of animality. But like everything we do, in our minds and sometimes out of them, we conjure up the possibilities of our dogs: maybe a doll baby, a work mate, a drover or a warrior. A little bit of imagination and the experience of *dog* can completely change the context of our feelings, our emotions, our lives. It is like being in charge of an infant human, all potential, unactualized, except as we inform that perspective with the cooperation of the human and the more-than-human animal.

In the best of circumstances, an individual human meets the individual dog in the gaze of cross-species curiosity, with some trepidation and eternal sacredness. As in the Greek tragedies, sacredness betrayed can become a fearsome place. For the most part, our eyes see a projection of dog, ignoring the context. How we colonize, how we fetishize, how we mythologize! We become very practiced in deconstructing and emptying the reality around the object of our focus. *Control*, we think, as we traipse on the edge of the unknown, trespassing upon the unseen, where everything is awkward and paradoxical. In this case, many hands, gazes and experiences went into the results that became Hex and Juno.

Now I represent another kind of unresolved experiential bizarreness, trying to make sense in recounting this trope of so long ago.

Julie Welker is dead. No ambiguity there. Hex was euthanized the night of the mauling. The owners of

Hex and Juno, those two neighbor attorneys, Boyd and Bowler, were an odd couple, to put it mildly: physically unattractive, the twenty-first century version of an inverted Archie and Edith Bunker, part bleeding heart liberals, part nerdy self-aggrandizers, part perverted sexual innuendo; but somehow, also do-gooder defense attorneys representing incarcerated people at the infamous maximum security prison, Pelican Bay State Prison (PBSP) in far northern reaches of California.

The breeding pair of dogs, Hex and Juno, were purchased from internet breeders by Peter "Redfern" Shrader while at Pelican Bay. He was operating an illegal dog fighting business during his three life terms, funded by settlements in abuse-of-civil-rights legal cases brought against the California Department of Corrections. The two attorneys, Boyd and Bowler, while residing down the hall from Julie in apartment 604, represented cellmates Shrader and Chip Stretch in those lawsuits. Both men, convicted felons—Stretch convicted of murder, Shrader of attacking a prison guard and knifing a defense attorney in court—were known ranking members of the Aryan Brotherhood gang at PBSP in Pelican Bay.

~~~

Of an average Pelican Bay prison population of 4,000, more than 25% are kept in solitary confinement, as these 1200 individuals are considered the most truc-
~~~

ulent of the imprisoned in the state. Often mere affiliation with a gang can earn you that brand and solitary residency at the supermax prison. These prisoners are held for twenty-two hours most days in what are called Secure Housing Units, known as SHU: a bunk and a sink with a toilet attached in a 7x11-foot windowless concrete cell. These cells are molded in blocks of eight so heavy they cannot be compromised. The blocks fit so tightly together that there is no mortar in the seams. The only opening in the room is the electronically operated door of thick grated steel with a finger-sized pattern in it. The dog pens in the San Francisco city animal shelter are just about half that size.

Daily, one at a time, in order to exercise, the incarcerated individuals spend an hour and a half in what is called "the dog run" in the center of the maximum-security pods at the facility, an indoor area approximately 12x12 feet with a skylight, their only exposure to natural light. Both Shrader and Stretch were held in the SHU.

The attorneys, Boyd and Bowler, befriended Shrader and Stretch, and even went so far as to legally adopt Peter Shrader in order to improve his protection under the law, should he become ill while incarcerated. When proxy caretakers for the dogs—missionary women who visited these and other incarcerated individuals at PBSP, one of whom boarded and trained the dogs on her farm in Oregon—were found lacking by Shrader in "toughening up" Hex and Juno, Boyd and Bowler offered to take the dogs to their one-bedroom apartment in San Francisco, just at the turn of the century. For protection. For protection.

"Cry 'Havoc' and let slip the dogs of war." This call from William Shakespeare in *Julius Caesar*, Act 3, echoed as Juno and Hex walked the streets of San Francisco, terrorizing their neighbors, fighting with other dogs, staring down neighbors in the elevator and on the street. Unfortunately, there was very little reported to police or animal control.

~

Within ten days of the deadly mauling, an administrative hearing was held as required by law to determine the surviving dog's status. Based on the testimony of various witnesses, Juno was declared vicious and ordered destroyed, but her fate was delayed as she was considered evidence in a police and grand jury investigation into the mauling and murder of Julie Welker.

Boyd and Bowler were indicted by a grand jury on charges of second-degree murder and manslaughter. After convictions, Thomas Boyd for manslaughter and Michelle Bowler for second-degree murder, the Presa Canario activist community (including a well-known dog whisperer) continued to seek Juno's release for more than a year. Dangerous dogs at the shelter in San Francisco, if they are able to be handled, may get an hour or so daily in a grassy fenced outdoor area, the exercise yard attached to the shelter. Juno never left her kennel. She was extremely agitated and aggressive within the kennel environment. She received daily socialization and enrichment time from a dedicated volunteer group who attend to long-term kenneled custody dogs at our shelter.

It would take a year for the conviction of Boyd and Bowler and two years before a Superior Court judge removed the stay on our motion to euthanize Juno, for humane as well as public safety reasons.

This event was a daisy cutter of a cultural bomb. A tragedy. A complex, difficult, multifaceted drama. The resulting media event lasted months. Reporters left no stone unturned; they dated shelter workers to get inside information, stalked volunteers, made threatening phone calls, seduced bureaucrats. Everyone had an opinion, as they do about animal issues. The story, already mind-boggling and weird, daily became even stranger. Lawyers blamed the victim for the dog attack on national TV, said she was wearing perfume, casting pheromones in the direction of Hex. There was a concatenation of news stories, each more crazed: pornography, bestiality, payoffs, bribery. Maybe we could repair this with a little hay wire.

The prisoner Shrader claimed Hex was his alter ego. Journals were found in his prison cell with drawings of Norse gods coming back to take revenge on doomsday. His cellmate Stretch got into the act with a dogman fantasy, and wrote and published two editions of *Man-Killer Dog War*, his retelling of the attack with drawings of Norse warriors and Hex leading armies into battle: "rebel–ution," he called it. Stretch was disallowed from publishing the books until a judge ruled he could donate his profits from the book to the Humane Society of the United States. He declined the opportunity to publish, as it would be colluding with the enemy.

In the meantime, there were results of this chaos.

Result 1

The case was moved to trial in Los Angeles due to the defense's contention that an unbiased jury could not be found in San Francisco. The jury in LA deliberated for eleven hours before they brought back guilty verdicts for both defendants. Thomas Boyd served three years. Michelle Bowler was released after serving seven years, then arrested again to serve another eight years due to an overturned sentencing by the original judge.

Result 2

Both Shrader and Stretch remain at Pelican Bay in the SHU at this writing.

Result 3

Welker's domestic partner prevailed in a landmark precedent-setting case and won the right to sue for the wrongful death of her partner. She sued the attorneys and the property owner of the apartment building and won in both cases. She set up a scholarship fund in Julie's name, for athletes at the private college where Julie had coached.

Result 4

Shelter workers and volunteers, to the last one, were struck with compassion fatigue. They lived through many debriefings and there were claims of PTSD that went to the EAP (Employee Assistance Programs), but this was a discomfort beyond healing, so full of ambiguity, paradox and confusion. The results for workers and volunteers, in a few words: shutdown, nightmares, drug addiction, alcoholism, change of career, even Buddhist conversion. In the end we all agreed to come to an adult perspective, whatever that meant; not reliving the past, perhaps. Employee assistance therapists were baffled, finally allowing specialists in post-traumatic stress to become involved with treatment. Alternative healing methods were approved.

Result 5

The California legislature changed state laws to redefine the obligations of owners who knowingly keep dangerous dogs.

Presa Canario is the short name for the dog breed that killed Julie Welker. *Presa* means prison in Spanish, or one captured, a feminine noun. Canario is Spanish for dog. From "Dog Island" or the Canary Islands, these dogs were originally bred as livestock working dogs. Now the Canary Islands are known for canaries, the bright little yellow birds that are sentries in the coal mines. When things begin to go haywire in the cave, they die.

Within a few months, the hay-baling continued to unravel, the Twin Towers were down, and we were overtaken by the spectacle of the invasion and bombing of Iraq. We called that "shock and awe." We didn't even think about baling wire; many, many canaries did not survive this mine.

Julie Welker was a daughter, lover, friend; a young, beautiful, vibrant athlete, a queer woman with her whole life ahead of her; and she was the canary trapped in front of her door on an early Friday evening in January of 2001, in a coastal big city by a bay. Now she is trapped in a sort of banal notoriety. With her and without her, we are all somewhat trapped in our self-created cave of memories, cave of mirrors, in this haywire mythology. Hounds of Hades greet us at the gates of the twenty-first century.

Euthanasia

Common usage of the word "euthanasia" often refers to injecting a cocktail of sedative and anesthetic drugs of overdose proportions into the vein of a beloved pet to bring about the merciful death of that being. When quality of life has diminished, it is believed, this intervention is necessary to prevent suffering. Others, like me, tack on "humane," calling it "humane euthanasia" to address the social problem of pet overpopulation in animal shelters all across the globe. Is this a linguistic cop-out, a euphemism? There is that "eu" again, meaning good: euphoria, Europe, eugenics. Euthanasia, meaning good death. Maybe. When you walk a physically healthy animal down the long hallway to the euthanasia room to alleviate a social problem, it seems there is a problem. For sure, it does not feel good, especially because you have been the caretaker of that animal for days or weeks or months.

When you think about it, when the same procedure is done to human beings on death row in the United States, we call that action an execution. Of 2,905 people on death row in the United States in 2016, twenty males were killed by lethal injection. A profile of those who were executed: member of an ethnic minority 58%, impoverished 99%, and more than 60% were inarticulate, uneducated, and initially without adequate representation.

It is believed that of the 1.2 million dogs euthanized in the United States annually, 40% are pit bull or pit bull mixed-breed dogs. There are many more of these dogs than there are homes to adopt them. This statistic for pit bulls, it seems, stands out because we have created an artificial culture for these type of companion animals, making them status symbols and for some, a projection of machismo. As hard as we try to unravel the myth, still many folks are hesitant to consider a pit bull-type dog for adoption or guardianship. Of course, poodles are status symbols, too. After major Hollywood films, Dalmatians, Chihuahuas, Saint Bernards and border collies became popular, and then overbred for a time.

In the wilderness, mountain lions are destroyed or relocated to protect the long-horned ram, and wolves are shot from helicopters to protect sheep in remote areas of Wyoming and Montana. In the Mississippi River, where invasive Asian carp were introduced into the river by us in the 1960s through the 1980s, these fish (some of whom weigh more than 100 pounds) have completely changed the river's aquatic profile. Now we are desperately trying to prevent those fish from entering the Great Lakes. In 2009, a fish poison (Rotenone) was used in a five-mile stretch of the Chicago Sanitary and Ship Canal to prevent this encroachment. Humans intervene in one way, then turn around years later and intervene in another.

Euthanasia is from the Greek *euthanatos*, meaning "easy death." Mercy killing, the operative emotion: compassion. Who decides? Easy for whom? Who commits the dastardly deed?

"Triage" comes from the French *trier*, meaning "to separate," and the word is used commonly for sorting out people based on their injuries, condition, or chances of survival when there is a scarcity of resources or an event that challenges transport to resources. Many countries have formalized standards for how to do that kind of grouping in the battlefield, in a mass casualty situation and/or in a disaster.

We saw up close what happened when life and death decisions were made in the aftermath of Hurricane Katrina (2005), courtesy of *New York Times* journalist Sheri Fink's book, *Five Days at Memorial*. Oxygen was rationed in Haiti after the 2010 earthquake. After World War I and during the Depression in the 1930s, eugenics theories espoused by influential people such as Helen Keller and Clarence Darrow allowed for sterilization and infanticide of "defective" babies, known as "the Black Stork movement" after Martin Pernick's film of that name. In the U.K., also during the '30s, a movement referred to as "Dignity in Dying" was established on a different, more compassionate note. In the United States, Dr. Kevorkian was to follow that movement, in somewhat jaded attempts to allow those on death row to choose fatal drugs in the name of science in his forty-year campaign for the right to die, which lasted until he was released from prison in 1999.

Death with Dignity laws have passed in California, Colorado, Oregon, Vermont, and Washington, D.C.; Montana and New Mexico have court-ruled euthanasia. At least ten countries including Germany, The Netherlands, Belgium, parts of Canada and Australia, allow for assisted suicide. Since 1940, Switzerland, among other nations, permits noncitizens to come to Switzerland for that reason. The U.K. has the "Society for Old Age Rational Suicide" (SOARS), established in 2009. Leave it to the Brits. And in an outlandish social event, Philippines President Duterte encouraged drug dealers and addicts to commit suicide, under a veiled threat that if they didn't, the state would execute them without trial. As reported by the Human Rights Watch, *World Report 2018*, at least 12,000 people had been killed through state-supported, drug-related murder by the end of 2017 in the Philippines.

Among cultural venerations, probably the most radical is the Church of Euthanasia, with the motto "Save the Planet, Kill Yourself." They also believe in the Unabomber Manifesto. (I'm not sure I get the connection.) Their online zine is called *Snuff It*.

⁓

As we know, rationing resources has become more common as the population of the Earth has grown, science has advanced, and human beings are in contact with all variety of bacteria and life-forms in almost every corner of the planet. Humans are organ recipients and surrogate mothers, and need dialysis machines and bone marrow transplants. Some drugs are being rationed, and in most of the world basic access to quality health care, including safe abortions, varies dependent upon income and location. The recent Ebola epidemic from 2013–2016 in West Africa previewed what is in store for us. If epidemic disease doesn't get us, illness, war, famine or old age certainly will.

Inability to treat ends in death. Hesitation to seek treatment also kills. Neglect kills. Secondhand smoke kills. Collateral damage. Civilians as human shields in war.

We turn away from death even while we know it is an essential part of life. "Death is as you believe," paraphrased from the Gospel of Matthew. "He who is not busy being born is busy dying," quoth Dr. Bob Dylan.

⁓

Let me tell you a story about *caenorhabditis elegans*, a nematode, a model multicelled invertebrate that survived the 2003 explosion of the Columbia spacecraft. This critter is very prominent in studies of aging. This small, one-millimeter-long roundworm has a short life span of only three weeks, the perfect specimen for scientists to observe and study coming to life, thriving and then dying. *C. elegans* lives in temperate soil, ideally in rich, composting organic matter. There are probably gazillions of them in the Bay Area of northern California. They have a fixed number of cells (989 hermaphrodites to 1,090 male cells, to be exact) and enlarge those limited cells to maturity. They emit an effervescent blue light at their death.

Following a growth spurt during their time as roundworms, *C. elegans* goes through a process known as apotosis (APE-oh-TOE-sis). Apotosis means the falling of leaves or flowers dropping petals. *C. elegans* has an "apototic predictability." Cell death-promoting genes are activated, which include necrosis, during which the cells are deprived of nutrients and energy. Other cell membranes become blurry, and fluid begins to fill intercellular space. This process encourages autophagy, which means consuming the cells from which other cells originate.

These processes happen all the time in many forms of life. Without them, the human body would expand beyond proportion. We would carry around a ton of bone marrow if our cells did not compost some of those differentiated bone marrow cells that are no longer vibrant. Your body's cellular structure is completely replaced in seven-year spans throughout your life. In other words, we are, all of us, living and dying simultaneously. Without this trade-off, when cells forget how to die, there is a condition that we call cancer.

Some of us who are dying or drawing near the death of our brains are soon to be living in a completely different form. Those of us with more time as an alive complex organism are hosting changes, living and dying cells, slowly and constantly throughout our lives.

The upshot of all these Nobel Prizes and scientific studies is that a single cell death-inhibitor has been identified. What does this mean for us, assuming that we persevere in attempting to control life and death? Predictably, this is the big takeaway: the commercial value of no gray hair, no loss of memory, sight or hearing, no voice changes or slower reflexes. Like the Hydra, we become the immortal species. We become the undead, the zombie, the parasite of our deep mythology, larger than life, something totally other. A new paradox, all right.

In the end, whether we are killing, aborting, triaging or rationing, it is all about context. Who are we and who are we euthanizing? It is about choice and values, and a lot about intent. But I guarantee you, it will never, ever be easy. Ethos, pathos, and compassion enter on both sides of the equation. When fully human and conscious, we may be able to acknowledge that we can become an agent of death as easily as an agent of life. It is happening whether we acknowledge it or not. We can only hope that death takes its inevitable place within a better balance for each of us.

But let's get back to euthanasia: All of the above is a soft way to approach hard facts. For me, euthanasia is very personal. The last time I had to request an animal put down was over the phone. I was in Chicago and my suddenly sick dog, Mini, a young poodle with an endearing underbite, a great personality and a characteristic hop in her step, was back in northern California, being cared for by a friend. Mini was unable to literally catch her breath. The veterinarians could not figure out what was going on with her. They had ruled out poison, mushrooms, pneumonia. They did a sonogram that showed nothing. Mini spent her last days under sedation in an oxygen chamber at the hospital, panting and gasping for breath. Finally, after no improvement, my options diminished, I asked for euthanasia. The veterinarian agreed.

Before Mini, Dulcea was the love of my life. She was a three-legged shepherd-Sheltie mix who had been left for dead in a ditch in Watsonville after being hit by car. After amputation of a back leg, she and I went on a long therapeutic journey to get her back on her feet, uh, paws. Dulcea used her tail as a rudder. She loved to run after squirrels, although she never caught one. Dulcea was ten years old when diagnosed with pancreatic cancer, with nothing much more to be done. As her life wound down, I bought a red wagon that rolled her along on walks and to work. She got cannabis and skullcap and rhodiola to help her through the pain of the cancer. She was fed wet dog food with bone broth. *As long as they are eating* is my mantra; as long as they are eating and can signal the need to urinate and defecate, and when an accident occurs, can remove themselves from the soiled area. As long as they can keep the food they eat in their stomachs. As long as there is some quality in their lives, and they are not in pain. Eventually the time was right.

Then came Gabriel. He grew up with Dulcea and was good friends with Mini. Gabe and Mini were quite the item walking down Valencia Street in San Francisco. He was an affable, handsome, sixteen-year-old golden retriever mixed breed who, before he died, could hardly see, hear, or get up from a prone position on his ample dog bed. Once an ambassador for his breed due to training and temperament, he taught postmen and PG&E guys, cops and the hospitalized, small children and fearful adults that dogs were not their enemy. Those rickety old legs used to jettison him down the beach after the ball. He loved the ocean. Once, Gabe could jump three feet off the ground for a high fly or a soft Frisbee. No longer able to maneuver his way out of the surf, we stopped going to the beach. Gabe had cataract eyes and multiple pink growths and tumors under all that blond hair. And yet, he still sniffed out the spot where last season's apples were rotting in the compost. *Not yet, not now.* Gabriel, named after the angel. We'd come a long way. *Not yet, not now.* Gabe lasted until the time was *now.*

The other very personal aspect of euthanasia is that I worked for many years in animal shelters in the cradle of progressive central coast California. I euthanized many animals, mostly dogs and cats. I also placed animals on the euthanasia list for others to kill. I drew up into the syringe the sedative called Rompun. I hydrated the powdered bottle of Fatal Plus. *Fatal Plus what?* I thought. Fatal is fatal. An oxymoron. Some beings were very sick or severely injured. Those were the easy ones.

Some were kind of sick; they had chronic ear infection, skin disease or diabetes. Others were only slightly injured; they had a cherry eye or a leg to be set. Many were healthy but had behavior issues and couldn't be trusted around kids, cats, or other dogs. Whether these issues were created by the shelter environment or predated their final stop at the local shelter was uncertain. There were always matters of space. Running out of space, having to move along the ones who hadn't found homes, hadn't been picked up by rescue, hadn't been able to walk up to the kennel cage door to make themselves known.

Herd management, the veterinarians call it. We have to do what is best for the greatest number. When the herd is separated (you remember that from triage, to separate), each one becomes an individual. After the long walk down the hallway, individuals meet individuals in the euthanasia room at shelters across this land.

~

As a result of having good teachers, I became an excellent euthanasia technician. They taught me that the essence of that excellence involved putting the animal first. That meant I had to hold my own thoughts and feelings steady and neutral during the procedure, suspend all outside stimulus, be 100% present in the moment, and meet that animal exactly where it was, receiving cues from him or her about what was needed to provide this being with a good death. This was how I respected them. I held myself as an instrument of the process, holding them in a regard and love so true that it was like a prayer. Once the needle was in, the drug ingested, and the weight of the animal fell into my chest or onto the table, "Come back a dolphin," I'd whisper. When I recounted this to friends, therapists or family, I'd say, "If this work has to be done, then it is a good thing it is me or someone like me."

~

There was not one day, not then and not now, that I don't think: *How can we stop this from happening?* As Bill Smith from the Mazer Guild (a nonprofit support group for euthanasia technicians) urged, "Just don't let them be born." And while it may happen less today, it is still happening. Yes, complex. Yes, education. Yes, competing interests. Yes, impossibly difficult in every respect.

The Live & Kicking Undead

In the fall of 2016, a couple of weeks before Hillary Clinton was defeated by Donald Trump in the presidential election, a friend and colleague from my days in animal welfare asked me to come back to work to help cover for her at Oakland Animal Services while she was out on unexpected health leave. Hesitant to emerge from a three-year, thoroughly enjoyed retirement even to assist her and her acting director, who was also a close friend and colleague I had mentored at the San Francisco City Shelter, I mulled over the offer. Somewhat allaying my doubts as I probed the specifics of the part-time position, suddenly everything fell into place: surprisingly reasonable, part-time housing nearby in a tight renters' market, flexible hours, and the advantage of bringing my two little white doggies to work with me at the shelter as well as in housing. And so, taking the path of least resistance while factoring in the benefits of extra cash to deal with unexpected tree work needed at home, I signed up for a six-month part-time management gig at the Oakland Animal Shelter.

Right away, within days of going back to work, many feelings arose for me. This prose poem outlines my raw attempts to round up the early disturbing turgidity I experienced.

Maybe I have been retired too long
You cannot just sit there
You will not believe the scene
One self says to another
A more detached
More professional self

Sixty-eight miles to the north
To the other side of the San Francisco Bay
There lies the East Bay
A directionless horizon of no vista
Consuming land like a hungry parasite
This alternate reality
The antithetic pathway
On a yellow-brick road

While driving, the collective testosterone
(Or is it adrenaline?)
Rises up in my torso
Surface-breathing lungs
Open mouth in marathon moan
Heart-pounding chest
Meeting the big rigs, delivery trucks
Appliance, repair, and garbage
While speedsters make desperate
Time behind tinted windows
Veering left and right
On the hit-and-run highway

To avoid the worst of traffic
I arrive before a polluted dawn
Gray-green shadows surround
Abandoned frayed dinosaur buildings
And many sets of railroad tracks
Stretch away from this place
Silence and caution greet me at the locked gates
Serving up the contradiction of bolted doors
and keyless entry
Met by soiled clothing, broken furniture
and shattered glass
Barking dogs and feral cats
The olfactory waft of farmyard rabbits

Inside, long corridors fluorescent lit
Another kind of dinosaur and tracks
Deliver me to a long day
Walking and talking
Computing and reading
Talking some more, the phone, the legislative alerts
The programs and applications
Email, letters, updates, complaints
Filling out multiple forms
And designing many, many others

Sarcasm, a way of being, is reintroduced and I
Shake her hand knowingly
We were never really on good terms but
There is something familiar about
Her swaggering deftness
Memory of that imposter
Reignites quickly and deftly

After dark the day is done
I am undone incomplete
Mind buzzing with tomorrow's weight
My left knee hurts like hell
For some reason I don't know
After Advil and ice packs even
Soreness under the cap and the
Thick vein pulsing and throbbing
Drained reflection of the ordered chaos

Tuna fish Quiznos on wheat
After dark escape
Put my knee up on ice
Check the Cubs game
And fall asleep on the couch
After the final limping dog walk

I dream deep about brothers and friends
In large wooden houses
Helping me carry logs
Buckets of coal
Prepare stone soup in cast iron
And dig out from snow mounds
Upon the wooden porch

It is winter
Not a leaf on the trees
The standing are stick figures
Birds have fled
Many are those who cannot hear my desperate call

Alarm buzzes me wake
Search for my spectacles
Removed, gaze a stranger in the mirror
Soapy steam in the shower
Barefoot and vulnerable

Afterwards, after words
My physical body expands
Filling the personage balloon
The slam of the car door
The engine responding

Accelerating onto surface streets
Red light, green light, no yellow
Brushing up against storefronts
Bike riders dash in early
Rush morning commute

At the entrance to the cyclone fence camp
Now I know the codes
I greet the detainees
Feeling their ghostly stares
I really don't know what to say
The door opens
Sensate space animates
A cloudy gray bedsheet with
Two round eyeholes
Crossing into present memory

~~~

It becomes a familiar feeling that I am tracked by unknown spirits, restless souls trailing me to work at the
~~~

Oakland Animal Shelter for those six long months. In the consistent loyalty required of familiarity, ghosts only appear when, as in a haunting, there is a pairing going on; a relationship or memories of one bring it all back to consciousness. As for me, the customary response of having been there, haunted by the déjà vu windy whistling and complexity, is a reminder of the contrast between *quaint* San Francisco Bay Area politics and the stark reality of the City of Oakland. The developing and sprawling Stanford/Silicon Valley/San Francisco technology boom has ramifications in the entire Bay Area but it has been catastrophic in Oakland. Attach that to police brutality, an inflamed public, a disastrous presidential election, the continuing and deepening division of haves and have-nots amid the wildfire of gentrification, and you end up with despair, anger, fear and paranoia, my own and others'.

These tired themes sat beside me in the passenger seat during my commutes and communes from Santa Cruz to Oaktown in the early morning hours of that dark winter in late 2016 and early 2017. The soundtrack varied in tone and cadence. I began listening to old tracks from California's own Kate Wolf singing about love: "Give yourself to love, love will have the answer." One month in, Trump was elected and I popped in a CD with a little Joni Mitchell tune, "Blue." Two months in, the Ghost Ship warehouse burned to the ground two blocks from the shelter, killing thirty-seven vibrant young artists in a vulnerable firetrap less than a block away from Oakland's central fire station. Lucinda Williams, *Down Where the Spirit Meets the Bone.* Three months in, city hall says there is a hiring freeze and no money. We can't even get license plates for new vehicles already purchased. Pink Floyd, "Money."

The detainees who were trying to survive the hostilities in the streets of Oakland, both human and more-than-human, were refugees of a poor economy or migrants from other states, other countries and other areas of the San Francisco Bay. The sheltered domestic animals brought in were companions, protectors or accessories. These attachments move both ways. When the expenses are too great, food costs too much, the humanoid becomes sick or must move away, or chooses to hang out with the wrong kind of friends, or gets arrested. For strike or bite, bark or defecation, the animals end up in the overcrowded kennels and pens.

The humans are detained in the confinement of Alameda County Jail(s), Oakland's massive, overcrowded, Santa Rita jail in Dublin, CA. It is not good to be a homeless and/or incarcerated person in this town. The backstory of Oakland, though, can be sought within a narrative of government ineptitude, police mismanagement and brutality, neglected streets, homeless encampments, poverty, and entrenched special interests trickling down with the worst consequences impacting the lowest common denominators, the poor and the animals. The domestic beings fare better than the immigrant or the wild.

~

The City of Oakland is full of paradox. The cliché, "the enemy of my enemy is my friend" is a cultural motto. Everyone is on high alert. Not to lose. Not to be disrespected. Not to be left behind. It seems like everyone plays this deadly game. What Oakland really needs is a tax base, a revenue stream that will fund the ambitious, sometimes utopian, progressive dreams of public servants and activists. The recent legalization of cannabis has brought some hope to Oakland and yet it is also another panoply of agitation and conflict. The gold rush is now the green rush. Who are the winners, who are the losers?

The City of Oakland has commissions and task forces and focus groups and support statements ranging from anti-slavery to pro-Palestinian, with nine sister cities: Fukuoka, Japan; Sekondi-Takaradi, Ghana; Dalian, China; Danang, Vietnam; Ulaanbaatar, Mongolia; Agadir, Morocco; Nakhodka, Russia; Ocho Rios, Jamaica; and Santiago de Cuba, Cuba.

In January 2019, the results of public relations market research indicated that the City of Oakland rated forty-ninth of fifty major United States cities as the best place to be employed. Homeless and homicide rates were among the highest in California. Rents had increased by 25 percent since 2015.

Another cliché, "out of sight, out of mind," works for both homeless humans and homeless animals. Thus, code enforcement (threats and intimidation) becomes the answer. However, the Oakland Police Department has been under a consent decree for racial profiling, brutality, extortion and corruption, its activities monitored by a judge for more than seventeen years.

The Hood Incubator, attempting to get more black and brown entrepreneurs involved in small businesses, ran up against well-intentioned politicians who in the end could not deliver on their promises. And a lot of time was wasted while nothing changes.

The East Bay includes the University of California Berkeley, Laney College, Mills College, the hills, and Mount Diablo State Park; there are the fancy enclaves in the hills and the elite live in Piedmont and Rockridge. The animal shelter for these areas is in the Fruitvale area of Oakland, four miles from downtown and two blocks from the Bay Area Rapid Transit station where Oscar Grant was murdered by BART police in 2009 on New Year's Day. The Fruitvale district is bordered by a disintegrated industrial area which has now become homeless encampments along the 880 and 580 freeways. The waterways of the western part of the Oakland are dissected by four separate sets of Amtrak commuter railroad trains coming and going. These tracks are all moving-away lanes (no station, no one is stopping here). Construction of the 29th Street/12th Avenue roadway bridge delivers the driver by freeway to the City of Alameda, the county seat.

Poverty, substandard housing and lack of oversight are consistent issues in Oaktown. On the right side of the bridge over the Oakland Estuary in Alameda (which is located on an island), somehow social justice issues are not so dire, maybe because of the bridge, certainly because of their tax revenues.

~~~

Oakland Animal Service (OAS) shelter remained under the oversight of the Oakland Police Department (OPD) for many years. As a result of federal investigation into corruption, the OPD has been under a consent decree since 2003 requiring court involvement in monitoring its operations, policies and procedures. Consent decrees usually last five years. This consent decree has been renewed three times, the latest in 2016, around an internal sex scandal and quid pro quo protection for prostitutes. The OPD has been in shambles for years, long before the consent decree kerfuffles. [At the time of this writing, the OPD continues to operate under the federal decree.]

The least of their flawed operation was that their data was not well organized. The animal data collected at the Oakland Animal Shelter was stored by and through OPD. This data is as essential in tracking dangerous individuals as it is in tracking dangerous dogs. In any event, the OAS data was incomplete, thin, lost or misplaced, and almost useless. As a result, the OAS mission of serving and protecting the residents of or visitors to the City of Oakland from bite dogs was a failure. And there were a whole lot of dog bites
~~~

in Oakland. Animals in need (sick or injured) were somewhat higher on the list of priorities for OAS, as bite reports became lost in the shuffle. Finally, in 2012–13 Oakland residents and concerned citizens rose up to get the animal shelter and services out from under the auspices of the police department. This was a good thing philosophically, but a setback physically and fiscally.

Within a month of my short-term rehire, reeling under the shock of the 2016 United States presidential election and fearful of the threat to sanctuary cities in the Bay Area, the City of Oakland froze their promised hiring and resources. As Oakland Animal Services was among underfunded departments, this outcome really hurt. But the OAS shelter was one among many difficult circumstances that arose during that time for the city and its constituents, both human and non-human. I did not want to have to go to city hall and beg for money to provide the bare minimum in service to these residents whose needs were so great. But there I was, in the eye of a storm. While engaged in political necessities on the side, my work time was spent trying to piece together a field-and-shelter response team that might actually put together a plan to attend to daily requests coming in from the community, on behalf of both humans and other-than-humans.

The takeaway for me in the Oakland experience is in what is called "bite dogs." These dogs have a history of biting, lunging toward, and growling at people and other dogs. When I arrived, the protocol for bite dog cases in Oakland was to build a record of complaints. If a lone incident was unprovoked and especially brutal, the response would jump the talking and accommodating phases and go immediately to a "dangerous dog" hearing, to determine whether a dog was to be considered "dangerous" and what restrictions would be placed on such a dog or dogs.

One fellow, call him Bob, had a history of owning and breeding nasty and aggressive dogs, maybe compensating for his small stature. In his mid-sixties, he was an eclectic mix of New Age hippie, motorcylist and misanthrope. He was very careful about his Atkins-based diet and thus he was careful about his dog's diets, for peak performance. Breeding mean mastiff/Staffordshire terrier pit bull-type dogs seemed to be an expression or extension of his virility. In some sense this was Bob's performance. By the time our paths crossed, Bob was in Alameda County Jail because he refused to follow a court order not to own dogs. He might have placed the dogs somewhere else, but that would mean he would have to take responsibility for them to be somewhere else. Let's be clear, that court order would likely result in his dogs being euthanized if he stayed in town.

In the meantime, his neighbors were through with Bob. They were really pissed off by the way Oakland officials had glossed over the problem with Bob and his dogs over a long time. For maybe ten years, he had been terrorizing his neighbors and their dogs with a variety of pit bull and pit bull-mix dogs at his residence in the Oakland hills. It was always multiple dogs who would break through the fence, charge through an opened front door, bark menacingly in a parked SUV in the driveway when neighbors passed Bob's house, or growl and lunge when neighbors talked to Bob near his front porch.

Bob lived in a modest neighborhood in the low hills above Oakland, his home inherited from his parents. Bob had no real interest or ability to keep up with the demands of maintenance and this home was now in general disrepair, which was also an issue for the neighbors, a mix of older established folks and young families with kids.

Bob had his priorities: the two humungous cherry Harley-Davidsons in the garage. He also had three 100-pound aggressive dogs in the house, one of whom was chained and locked in the basement. He advertised himself as a dog breeder, behaviorist and trainer, and he apparently believed that.

Initially, in 2004, Bob read a story in the paper about an aggressive white pit bull who had attacked a woman and her dog in a park in Oakland. Because ownership of dangerous dogs is a matter of public record, Bob was able to contact the owner of the bite dog and ask for one of her female puppies. Bob named his dog Luna, and thus the story begins.

In 2005, Luna went for a walk with Bob. When he let her off leash, she attacked a medium-sized dog in a San Francisco park. Bob called his dog off the other dog, calling her by her name. Bob and Luna took off. The owner of the other dog later gave a description of Bob to the San Francisco Bite Unit of the San Francisco Police Department and named Luna as the aggressor.

Luna was an angry dog and Bob liked that about her. He taught her to pull on ropes and leather belts until they were shredded. It is believed Luna even bit Bob a few times. After that first incident, Bob bred Luna to a mastiff-type dog that belonged to a friend of his. In 2006, Luna had a litter of six puppies and Bob kept the three brindle ones. Best we could tell, he started advertising and selling adolescent puppies that he claimed were trained as service animals for protection and diabetic medical alert, a bogus claim, as the dogs were neither trained nor socialized.

About this time, the complaints started coming in from the neighbors in east Oakland: barking dogs, lunging dogs, people couldn't walk by the house. Kids were not allowed to play in otherwise quiet streets around Bob's house. After their dog was killed, one of Bob's neighbors moved to get away from worrying about their kids on the other side of a shared fence, taking a huge financial loss on their property. Bob was sued three times. And Bob lost three times.

More incidents began to surface and accumulate: In 2008, Luna almost killed an Australian shepherd dog in Oakland. This was covered by the local press, and Bob and Luna could not get away this time. Oakland Animal Services advised the owner of the Australian shepherd to treat it as a civil matter and sue Bob, which he did, winning all expenses and a settlement. A dangerous dog hearing was held; Luna was declared dangerous and ordered to be muzzled when in public and kept in a kennel in her yard. Bob said he was moving to San Francisco.

At the end of 2008, a second incident in San Francisco occurred on a Golden Gate Park running trail when three dogs (a white pit bull and two brindle mastiffs) attacked a young man and bit him several times. This time passersby got involved, called an ambulance for the victim, and held Bob by force until the SFPD arrived. Because Bob gave his Oakland address, the San Francisco PD called Oakland Animal Services and asked for a history on the dogs. There was no history, they were told. Yes, the dogs were licensed.

In the evening in late July of 2011, two dark-colored dogs in front of Bob's house attacked a woman who was new to the neighborhood. She fought off the dogs, covering her neck. She thought she was going to die. Bob came out of his house and tried to pull the dogs off the woman. After being dragged by the dogs some distance down the street, she miraculously survived, though with multiple dog bites and scraping injuries.

Bob claimed he was a good Samaritan, that they weren't his dogs, that he didn't know them. The resulting lawsuit ended in a settlement overwhelmingly in her favor.

Bob was so like Donald Trump, loving the drama, the risk, thriving in chaos; Bob was a narcissist. Everything was always about him: his freedom, his rights, his property. When other beings depend on you to do the right thing as parent, neighbor, friend, caretaker, guardian or steward, it is important you take the time to acquire some knowledge about what that responsibility entails. Under order, Bob took his dogs to a trainer, boarded them for months at her kennel, and asked her to make them more sociable. She found his dogs aggressive and unruly to the point that she advised him to give them up. Of course, Bob adamantly refused. He changed their names, calling them each other's names and licensing them in other counties to obfuscate their identities and his address.

The scam continued. More dog attacks occurred. More negligence. More lying. Bob licensed his dogs to a false address 125 miles away in Sonora. He listed them as "service animals," who are given special privileges under state law. Without going much further into it, Bob was a fraud at minimum and likely a sociopath at worst.

~

In the end, we were able to contact the people who were caretaking his dogs while he was in jail. We found that the extent of their care involved visiting Bob's three dogs at his residence for about an hour and feeding them once daily, according to caregiver statements. We argued that this was inadequate care and called for a welfare check. We contacted his attorney, who lived in Santa Cruz. We arranged to meet the attorney and the caregiver one weekday morning at the residence for the welfare check.

The attorney didn't show up that morning, but we convinced the caregiver that we had the legal right to inspect, providing an email giving the attorney's permission. Due to inadequate care, conditions in the house, the fact that the dogs were alone in the house for up to 23 hours a day, and the way they were kept locked in separate rooms with one chained in the basement, we had plenty of reason to remove the dogs. And no choice but to take them back to the shelter.

After Bob was released from jail, we held dangerous dog hearings that upheld OAS actions and kept the dogs in our custody. Finally, we went to Superior Court, where the judge told Bob he could no longer own dogs. The neighbors were very relieved. There was some overdue justice that day in Alameda Superior Court, but no end to the chaos. And the lives of victims, human and dog, were strewn among the discord.

On that very day, Trump came out with the Muslim Travel Ban 3.0; Hawaii quickly filed a legal challenge, requesting a temporary injunction against the order.

During my time at the Oakland Animal Shelter, it was filled to the brim with companion animals. More than three-quarters of the dogs over forty pounds in the shelter were pit bull and American Staffordshire terrier-type dogs (in the pit bull family). The rest were German shepherd and Rottweiler, with a few Labrador retrievers and huskies mixed in. Of the many little dogs who weigh less than twenty-five pounds, three-quarters of these were Chihuahua or mixed terrier/ Chihuahua. The rest were terrier mixed with poodle, Maltese, Shi Tzu or Pomeranian. The dog census was split between these two major sizes, breeds and weights; middle-weight dogs were scarce indeed. There were more than fifty mostly adult cats and a few kittens in early April, 2017. Two guinea pigs, twelve rabbits, three roosters, a goose, and a boa rounded out the census.

Animal caregivers and officers made up the majority of the Oakland Animal Services (OAS) staff of thirty-five workers. The rest were administrators, managers and support staff. Like the San Francisco shelter, the Oakland shelter had a diverse workforce: Pacific Islander, African American, French, Mexican American, Filipino and Chinese with a narrow sprinkling of white women and men, mostly at the top. The line staff was solidly working class, with high school diplomas and blood relatives as coworkers. It was surprising how many couples and siblings (nepotism is alive) work in these city entry-level jobs that pay comparatively well but are brutal emotionally, physically and spiritually for a young person's first job.

If you want a vivid picture of an existential crisis in youth, visit Oakland Animal Services.

Most of the animal enrichment efforts were created and completed by a volunteer staff of more than one hundred, an urban/suburban cadre of committed, value-driven, highly educated animal lovers, mostly middle-aged white women. Stakeholders included the activists among these volunteers: Friends of Oakland Animal Shelter (FOAS); the Oakland SPCA, a well-endowed humane society a half mile away; rescue clubs for various purebred dogs and cats; humane groups from as far away as Oregon and Washington state; and a restaurant that would take, show and place geriatric, sick and ill cats.

The current campus of the Oakland animal shelter was built in the 1990s. Designed by well-regarded shelter architect George Meier, it was then considered top of the line. Thirty years later, under the auspices of the Oakland Police Department during most of that time, the Oakland Animal shelter was showing its age and beginning to fall apart. The volunteer artists and activists from FOAS did their darnedest to spruce up the lobby, paint murals, and make the outside of the shelter more attractive to visitors. But behind the murals and waxed lobby floors, the cyclone fencing and concrete floors no longer obscured the physical as well as psychic remnants of the tortured ends of too many lives.

For my part, officially and superficially, I was trying to put out fires and just get folks the correct information, operating procedures, forms and supplies to reasonably do what is expected of them, to do their jobs.

My spirit had something else in mind. My body was unprepared to resume this complex assignment, though I'd had thirty months of relaxation and recuperation in retirement. I had been reading, writing, "inseeing" (poet Rainer Maria Rilke's term for deep empathy for other species), distilling and insighting for months. I was becoming a verb: a *being*, not so much a human who was doing.

Maybe I really had prepared, feeling more than ever that this work invitation was both awful and inviting. I'd spent so much time cultivating a reemergence of my good sense and nature, learning to know the land that I live on as well as I used to know the contents of files on my desk at work.

In Oakland, I'd become reacquainted with scofflaws, horses in rain, abused wildlife, the threats of politicians and bureaucrats, bullying, incompetence, and the challenges of city hall. And Bob. I recognized that familiar feeling of willingness to meet people where they are, to simply represent the animal's interest, and the willingness to problem solve, holding competing interests, though I did not always do that successfully.

And not one minute too soon, it was all over. I searched and searched for some political theory that would explain what was happening in Oakland, what happened to me in Oakland, this hipster place in the advanced Bay Area that was going through the machinations of growth and gentrification while paused in lost revenue, failed industry and corrupt land development deals. On the list of cities with the highest crime rates and the most diversity, a launchpad for hip hop and the West Coast Blues, home of the Black Panthers, the Oakland A's, the Raiders, Jerry Brown and Jim Jones. Of course, it is not solely Oakland where this is happening. It is all over these United States, residing uncomfortably within our truly divided states of mind.

We live in an open system, constantly exchanging energy and matter with our surroundings. All our surroundings. All beings.

I hope to have described the shape of the Oakland Animal Services shelter in its form as I experienced it. However, from my view, the real matter in Oakland is much more about the formless…the drifting gray sleepiness, the pointy hat and masked identity. The bedsheet. And yes, the double entendre with white supremacy and the Klan is not inadvertent.

The shelter is in the form of a melting glacier, a hard-edged, frozen-in-time physical entity no longer up to the task, a past flow that is disintegrating. In endless movement and concern, staff warm up the icy edges, trying to keep the place clean, sanitary and free from disease, providing for the dogs and cats in their care. In the full high heat of overwork and intense emotion, the melting ice condenses, becoming a mist, the formless. Those spooky and troubled souls, both human and more-than-human, chase around one another in a ghostly labyrinth, the image of a cloudy gray bedsheet with eyeholes undulating in the sailing, blustery wind wherein floats the released energy, what remains of the undead. A ghoulish metaphor that may fit for all of Oaktown…where unrest is continuous in constant struggle for freedom and justice.

⁂

Animal rights and animal welfare are nonpartisan issues. Each of us is stumped and awed by jarring episode(s) in our lives—on the road, in the mountains, on the street, or in our emotions—when we confront animism, the animal in us and outside of us. We share the incidents, coincidence or emotion with our relations, Animalia, all of us beasts from a blastula while embryo develops.

If we pay attention to the panoply of critters toward whom we cast our glance, sometimes in fear, confrontation, frustration or impatience, those relatives will awe or surprise us. Often we are met with indifference. However, with mindfulness and empathy between us, within the calm of an even gaze, curiosity can be exchanged, and most of all, *regard*. This honoring, this enchantment of each other, is a common denominator, even in the fear brought forward by a snarling growl or the revulsion accompanying pungent, greasy fur coats, maggoty wounds or white bones protruding from flesh on a mangled leg.

On the other hand, these creatures lie close to us in our homes and in our settled environment. These domestic animals become a bridge across the river of differences into an opening full of love for the Other. When one of them looks, *really looks* at one of us, that creature reveals: *I am of you as you are of me*. In that uncertain, ghostly stare where our pairing occurs, I bid you to return the quiet gaze, look into the opening, and be ready for mutual *bewilderness*.

PTSD:
Picking the Scab Darnit

These experiences from twenty-odd years ago still make me cry out in the night, ever stirred and horrified.

Julie, the large, hundred-pound-plus mixed-breed brown and black old soul at five years old, the shepherd-Rottweiler who leaned against my thigh as I leashed her to walk her out of her cage for euthanasia. No one wants a five-year-old big dog. She said to me, coming from somewhere deep and resonant: *I forgive you. It is not your fault. Not only do I forgive you but I love you for your great sensitivity, care and courage.*

In the middle of the night, Mitsy, a small, white and tan spaniel-type dog, was HBC (hit by car) on Highway 1 near Buena Vista, her skull cracked open. I cradled her head in my hands as I watched the bloody brain tissue ooze from her wound. She remained conscious as I carefully placed her in the front seat of my animal control vehicle. I held her paw during the trip to the emergency veterinary hospital. She looked panicky initially, trying to lift her head; I talked softly to her, saying what a good dog she was to let me touch her at all, and she was soothed and relaxed some. Soon only her eyes were moving as she became unable to move, deeply in shock and near death as I pulled into the driveway of the animal hospital.

Arriving at a house in the circles on the west side of Santa Cruz where, to my dismay and utter disbelief, an educated middle-class bearded young man told me that he had pitchforked an opossum because he feared her. He showed me where the still-alive opossum was now pinned through the belly in the dirt in the backyard of his house. He wanted her immediately removed because he believed the opossum would harm his new baby. A young woman, wide-eyed and tense, stood behind the screen door with an infant in her arms, nodding her head in agreement. I unpinned the trapped opossum, now bleeding from the mouth, and found that this mother opossum had three baby opossums in her pouch.

On Freedom Boulevard, a hit-by-car deer with both back legs fractured in multiple places struggled helplessly to right himself off the shoulder and into a ditch full of Scotch broom, prickly berry vines and poison oak. There was no way I could approach him safely. Eventually a highway patrol officer shot him at close range with his revolver. For penance, I threw myself into the ditch and dragged the dead deer out to the roadside and my van. Passersby helped me put his still-warm body into the back compartment of the vehicle. We all cried at the stunned look on his face and the pure panic left in his searching eyes.

~~~

Rolling up to a house in Felton off Highway 9, onto one of those little side roads by the streams and creeks that feed the San Lorenzo River, to see a young German shepherd dog hung by a heavy braided rope, swinging from an unusually low branch of a huge old-growth redwood tree. His weight pulled down on the limb so that his hind paws brushed the earth, the swaying redwood leaves mourning and genuflecting above in a light breeze. This reminded me of the song "Strange Fruit," an earworm that played incessantly in my head for months.
~~~

The Day the Chickens Almost Saved My Knees

To the point: some of my best friends are chickens. My first good friend chicken was a handsome Polish hen named Tina, after Tina Turner. With a prolific head of speckled feathers that burst above her like a full-blooming dahlia, doubling her height, Tina was lanky, a spotted tan and brown highlighted with sparkling umber. Her morning voice softly buck-bucked in harmony with the doves, her tender song drawing up the sun. I had lived among other chickens, Ameraucana and Auraucana, Rhode Island Red, Barred Rock and Leghorns. But Tina was a good friend. She acted like a goose, squawking and cackling when strangers approached. She followed along while I was outdoors doing chores. She would stay far away when I fired up the chainsaw. I swear I saw Tina's little forehead furrow in the assault of that noise.

Otherwise, Tina was an outdoor companion. She'd quickly look away and take off in exaggerated half flight when I'd notice her underfoot, then soon would be back, pecking the dirt for grubs, watching sidelong to make sure she wasn't in my way. She was very shy among her own species, an introvert, one might say. Tina didn't lay many eggs. But she had character, voice, and a great personality.

The other truly amazing chicken I knew and befriended was Amelia the Rhode Island Red, her looks unremarkable, a common hen. I came to know her only for a short time. Amelia, a young chicken but not exactly a spring one, was rescued from power lines in the Western Addition in San Francisco on a quiet Sunday in 2003. Amelia had been launched in a cheap white rattan basket attached to a large bunch of helium balloons, a public relations stunt for a Japanese tech company. The gas balloons lofted her into the air early that summer morning. By 10 am there were calls to San Francisco Police Department, Northern Station and to Animal Services to rescue a chicken in a basket tangled and hanging from the power wires near Sutter Street, abutting the tony Pacific Heights neighborhood.

A crowd gathered as streets were closed, traffic was diverted and the fire department arrived. The first responders in all their heavy fire gear shook their heads, unconvinced they could help; the basket was tangled in live power lines. There was Amelia, frozen but very alive in that basket thirty feet above the pavement. The power company's emergency crew was contacted. It would mean a significant power outage for an hour or more for more than 100,000 San Francisco resident customers. "But here we are, in the City of St. Francis," we argued. Things lined up.

The fire department brought its big ladder truck and held it at the ready. PG&E called their power plant and received permission to turn off the power. The Animal Control Officer climbed the ladder behind the fireman and plucked Amelia out of the gondola-type basket. The balloons were popped and heavy balloon strings were cut from the wires. Power was quickly restored. Amelia's experience in an aerostat, an aircraft lighter than air, was over by 4 pm that afternoon, with a cheering crowd below.

However, Amelia was open-beak breathing, shivering in terror, completely freaked out, her temperature and pulse elevated. (It is hard to take a pulse on a chicken, as they are always quite nervous.) Her one-sided look at me as I carried her down the aisle to the medical clinic was worried. Both of us sighed. Our veterinarian gave her a light sedative and staff took turns keeping watch over the rescued Amelia.

The next morning the story was covered in the *San Francisco Chronicle* and the story went viral. Soon the press, cable news, and major stations CNN and NBC were calling for interviews. A live interview set up for 4 am San Francisco time the next morning would be with Katie Couric and Matt Lauer, for one of the New York morning shows. Amelia, however, was not ready for prime time. She was recovering from her ordeal.

I stood in her stead on national TV with the officer on the scene. We did fine. We had those earbuds and shirt mikes that made us look normal. Inadvertently, I made a joke on the air about Amelia, the chicken, narrowly escaping being "fried." Both Matt and Katie laughed and so did a whole panoply of technicians in the, ahem...wings. In a regrettable oversight that still haunts me as spokesperson for some of my best friends, I forgot the main message: There are tens of thousands of chickens available for adoption in local animal shelters all across the United States. Go to your shelter and adopt a hen!

During the pending cruelty investigation, Amelia's cage was placed in a quiet corner in my office and she began a soft clucking. An anonymous tipster told us that four other chickens had shared Amelia's fate. We held a press conference asking for information and witnesses, but apparently only Amelia had the good fortune of being seen, retrieved and recovered. The others probably perished in the San Francisco Bay or surrounds. When the investigation fizzled, the goal was to find Amelia a home. After forty-eight hours, with lots of media attention, Amelia had calmed down and even begun laying eggs. Our veterinarian maintained there were to be no photos or TV interviews for Amelia.

A week later, Amelia was up for adoption. With much fanfare, we proclaimed her ready for a relationship. People from all over the Bay Area, the United States, the UK and Australia responded. Ultimately, Amelia was placed with a woman from Santa Rosa who promised organic food, other chickens, and separate quarters until Amelia was accepted into the existing flock. She was inspiring, that Amelia; she was a survivor. And she was representative of all the chickens who make their way to animal shelters across the United States.

~~~

Here's the subtext of these chicken stories. A few years into retirement, I began having consistent knee pain due to osteoarthritis, bones rubbing under and around my kneecap. This condition is a result of the meniscus lubricant drying up after years of pounding and weight bearing, shrinking the space between the kneecap and the top of the knee joint. Gravity and general aging conspire, after seventy years, to use up that fluid. For a long while I just lived with it, and like all delusions living within denial, the pain got worse. I began researching possible resolutions: glucosamine, steroid injections, arthroscopic interventions, total knee replacement...and then, *voila!* Who knew that hyaluronic acid could help knee pain? Hyaluronan is a natural, organic substance found in joint cartilage and the synovial fluid in our joints. And my discovery was that this substance was made from the combs of chickens.

This appealed to me, I can't say why. I'm a vegetarian (although I do eat fish occasionally) and an animal person. But I began wearing my rust-colored Kauai t-shirt with the rooster on it as a way to honor the fowl in my life and ask for guidance. I read more.
~~~

SUPARTZ FX therapy is an injectable solution made from highly purified sodium hyaluronate (also known as hyaluronic acid) extracted from chicken combs. These are harvested from chickens that have been certified as suitable for human consumption via pre- and postmortem veterinary inspection.

During a triad series of injections over a few weeks, the chicken and the chicken comb reentered my life in a new way. The gift of animal bodies somehow seems okay, even fitting, a way of acknowledging our interdependence upon one another. Whether pig valves, horse urine, snake venom, worms, frogs, horseshoe crab blood or bee stings, the animal as medicine is just one facet of a reality we share with them, while wrestling with a clearer view of the existing power imbalance.

In earlier days, chickens like Tina and Amelia had given me hope, provided inspiration. Together we had exchanged energy and a great deal of mirth. On that day just months ago at this writing, the unnamed, unknown chickens and their combs saved my knees. Some of the best chickens, with or without names, remain not only friends, but saviors. Today I honor them and I thank them.

~

Fryer or roaster, baked, boiled or battered. Some forty animal liberation protesters were arrested at Petaluma Farms in Sonoma in late May of 2018. This was another episode in a long line of animal rights actions. They say: Eating animal flesh is not okay. I wonder if they know that every vaccine, insulin, and many other lifesaving treatments depend on the contributions of our animal and plant friends.

Our dependence on animals has a profound influence on the quality of human life and numerous benefits for our health, for our survival. Maybe it has to do with *how* we regard their gift of a better, longer, healthier life. *How we treat them. How we care for them. How we know them.*

In facing this complex issue, we are just beginning.

Initiation
Part II

As part of my self-care regimen over the years of working as a professional amateur in animal welfare, I practiced the art of tai chi, a Chinese exercise with origins in Taoist nature philosophy, involving the integration of mind, body and spirit. At the change of the millennium, I began my flirtation with ink and tattoo art and now have five tattoos, all about chi, also spelled *qi*, (meaning life force or life energy): two mirror images of Cloud Hands calligraphy (my tai chi club's name) on the inside of each forearm, a chipmunk on my right shoulder, a chickadee on my left shoulder, and a chicken, a silver spotted Sussex, on the back of my neck. *Qi, qi, qi, qi, qi*... I'd say when people asked, pointing to my tats.

When camping recently in the Eastern Sierras, during a day hike in the middle of nowhere, I was surprised again by a little chipmunk who brought my chipmunk lore, experiences and initiations back to me, delivering them vividly and in a different way;

I could say they even brought the possibility of fresh chipmunk conversations, synchronicities and messages to mind. The idea of open understanding and communication with other species and other life forms expanded in my animal welfare work and seems more feasible since my retirement, what I called my jubilation, after thirty years in animal welfare. Since my repose, I'd been in contact in dreams, visions and fantasies with a variety of beings, from insects and trees to bodies of water.

Walking on a lightly used trail near Virginia Lakes, away from the fast-running feeder creek and parallel with a clearly marked path below, a chipmunk appeared to my left along the trail. Sitting up, she seemed to greet me. Stopped in my tracks and breathing deeply, in accordance with current theories in neuroscience about calm and safety in the mammalian nervous system as a way to encourage communication with other species, I signaled to her my intention of witness and curiosity, quietly relaxing my face into a soft smile.

She appeared fine with this and began digging a hole just off the path, looking for food, variously sitting up, completely ignoring me and bringing unidentified morsels to a tiny pert mouth, chewing quickly, then going back to work digging. She got so into this excavation that her belly lay flat in the hole and her back legs pumped and splayed behind her. Those back legs were amazing, almost as long as her body with long sharp nails at the end of her paws. I got to see how she was able to sit up, kangaroo-like on her haunches, peering about as she consumed her finds. Recognizing that her metabolism was racing in exertion, I deepened my breathing, encouraging each of us to calm even further. Time slowed down. My mind was able to memorize the details of our engagement. The detail with which I was able to view this beautiful and intelligent little striped being formed within me a perspective I had never known with an animal in the wild.

Her tail acted as a dusty sentry, twitching as her head was completely submerged in the soft earth, pine needles and decayed cones. The fur of her coat was amazing: two sets of stripes on either side of her torso in bright contrast against the smooth undappled purity of tan, like a running board up her back to her neck, where the color and hue abruptly changed. The fur at the top of her head was smooth as marble. She sported a reddish-tinged short silky cap over her skull, ears and eyes. When she came up for a breather, I impulsively pushed up my sleeve and showed her my tattoo. She was a small western *Tamais* chipmunk, a mountain chipmunk, about half the size of the image on my upper arm.

Then came a rapid, intense hawk *scree* and she dashed into the chaparral and low underbrush alongside the path, away from the pine needles. Collecting myself and listening for the raptor, I walked farther down the trail another mile or so, the woods notably quiet since the hawk's announcement. Reflecting on our meeting upon my return along the path over an hour later, you won't believe this: *A western chipmunk came before me on my left once more.* She crossed the path in front of me, sat up, looked at me and gestured to another chipmunk coming upon the path to my right. I was astonished to now encounter two chipmunks, one of whom I recognized because of the way I had studied her markings earlier. And now there was another, sisterly being, I believed, because markings though similar were not quite the same, and this new one was maybe slightly smaller.

Incredible, I thought as I became still and watched this second chipmunk dig and forage along the path. She dug with great vitality, digging deep until she was upside down and belly up in the hole she excavated, almost like she was showing me how it was done, what trusting, reckless abandon looked like. *There are many of us*, she seemed to say, *who can show you.*

Her cream-colored belly was ruffled with rabbit-like fur and the clawed toes at the end of her back legs pawed the air. She righted herself, surfacing with some sort of nut or seed or possibly fungus, I couldn't tell for sure. Something delectable. As I pulled oxygen deep into my belly, to memorialize this unusual assembly, I invoked the spirits to guard her and her family safely, while she held the prize in her front paws and delicately feasted. Reverent, still and silent, I mused over their apparent relationship to one another and then to me, asking myself: *Why would they show up for me?* Homo sapiens and Rodentia passing in the light, fellow travelers in conference. I showed this second chipmunk my tattoo also. She was thoughtfully unimpressed as she kept eating. *The real thing...* she seemed to say as she nosed the air and put her head back in her very own dusty path.

After a time, as it was getting late, I returned to camp, wondering if these chipmunks were signaling me, gatekeepers of a sort for a journey I am to take, or a journey I had taken, or a door opening to acknowledge passage, or a signpost toward an unknown destination. And yet the fable before me was a sacred and mysterious experience, just perfect as it unfolded. No analysis. *The real thing.*

I have felt a curious contentment and slightly unhinged at the same time since these new chipmunk friends came before my eyes. It is a similar feeling of relief and yes, awe and magic as well as fear, that I first felt at my chipmunk initiation so long ago, holding these apparently contrary feelings in chorus. These thoughts, emotions, realities—songs even—point the way and will lead me, through me to you, could lead us, can lead us if we follow willingly, into and out of the known straight and narrow path, across linear time, into the spiraling vertical and imaginal space/time where boundaries blur.

Reduction

Only questions remain. And some good quotes. This quote stands out:

> *"Not everything that is faced can be changed, but nothing can be changed until it is faced."*
>
> –James Baldwin

Post-face

What is to be learned of all those unrecognized faces?

"Who is grievable?" asks philosopher and public intellectual, Judith Butler.

Who is less *being*? Who is more *being*? Who is grievable? Isn't every *being* grievable?

Backward/Toward

Things work until they no longer work. Some things never really worked but we were in denial or too busy. We can do better than we have thus far.

What does it take to walk the middle path, to move consciously on Earth? What does it take to do no harm, to create a new narrative?

Listen for the *anima mundi*, the soul of the world, for there is a message for us: true regard and agency for all beings. Only then will we comprehend the collective, fragile, fathomless, and profound interdependence of all our relatives.

CPSIA information can be obtained
at www.ICGtesting.com
Printed in the USA
FSHW010718270521